MATH 1100

CUSTOM EDITION FOR NORMANDALE COMMUNITY COLLEGE

Taken from
Mathematical Ideas, Eleventh Edition
by Charles D. Miller, Van E. Heeren, and John Hornsby

Custom Publishing

New York   Boston   San Francisco
London   Toronto   Sydney   Tokyo   Singapore   Madrid
Mexico City   Munich   Paris   CapeTown   Hong Kong   Montreal

Taken from:

Mathematical Ideas, Eleventh Edition
by Charles D. Miller, Van E. Heeren and John Hornsby
Copyright © 2008 by Pearson Education, Inc.
Published by Addison-Wesley
Boston, Massachusetts 02116

This special edition published in cooperation with Pearson Custom Publishing.

Printed in the United States of America

10 9 8 7 6 5 4 3 2 1

2009360812

LA

**Pearson
Custom Publishing**
is a division of

www.pearsonhighered.com

ISBN 10: 0-558-30285-8
ISBN 13: 978-0-558-30285-6

CONTENTS

Taken from *Mathematical Ideas*, Eleventh Edition, Charles D. Miller, Van E. Heeren, John Hornsby.

1

COUNTING METHODS

When two dice, each with six possible faces, are tossed, there are $6 \cdot 6 = 36$ ways the dice can land. This is an application of the *fundamental counting principle* introduced in this chapter.

The game of craps, which involves finding the *sum* of two faces, is a mainstay in gaming casinos. A win occurs if the first roll is a natural (7, 11), and a loss occurs if it is craps (2, 3, 12). If a point is rolled (4, 5, 6, 8, 9, 10), it must be repeated before a 7 is tossed in order to win. If 7 is tossed before the point, you lose. (*Source*: www.ildado.com/craps_rules.html)

Craps was popular among U.S. servicemen during World War II. In the Oscar-nominated 1941 movie *Buck Privates*, Bud Abbott and Lou Costello perform one of their many comedy routines on the silver screen, with Costello getting the better of Abbott by twisting around the rules of the game. Later mathematics-related scenes appear in the movie as well, one involving a money-changing scheme and the other a word problem dealing with the ages of Costello and a little girl.

1

Most questions addressed in this chapter will contain a phrase such as "How many . . . ?" or "In how many ways . . . ?" or "Find the number of. . . ." In effect, such a question asks for the cardinal number of some particular set. There are many possible reasons for knowing the number of elements in a particular set. One major reason is to be able to calculate the likelihood that some event may occur, that is, the *probability* of the event.

For example, the genetic code of an individual human consists of approximately six billion DNA bases stored in a linear sequence. The nucleus of every cell contains a copy of this code, tightly coiled in the shape of a double helix. Because each base in the sequence can be any one of four types, called adenine (A), guanine (G), thymine (T), and cytosine (C), there are approximately $4^{6,000,000,000}$ different sequences possible. Of this huge number, only .1% to 1% is unique to the individual, with 99% to 99.9% being common to all humans. The probabilities used in DNA profiling are based on the tiny .1% to 1% that is unique.

The cardinal numbers of some sets are easy to find. Others are more difficult. Some are so large, or so involved, that even state-of-the-art computers cannot determine them. A number of methods are developed in this chapter that are useful in answering "How many . . ." questions.

1.1 Counting by Systematic Listing

One-Part Tasks • Product Tables for Two-Part Tasks • Tree Diagrams for Multiple-Part Tasks • Other Systematic Listing Methods

Counting methods can be used to find the number of moves required to solve a Rubik's Cube. The scrambled cube must be modified so that each face is a solid color. Rubik's royalties from sales of the cube in Western countries made him Hungary's richest man.

The methods of counting presented in this chapter involve listing the possible results for a given task. This approach is practical only for fairly short lists. When listing possible results, it is extremely important to use a *systematic* approach, or we are likely to miss some results.

One-Part Tasks The results for simple, one-part tasks can often be listed easily. For the task of tossing a single fair coin, for example, the list is *heads, tails,* with two possible results. If the task is to roll a single fair die (a cube with faces numbered 1 through 6), the different results are 1, 2, 3, 4, 5, 6, a total of six possibilities.

EXAMPLE 1 Selecting a Club President

Consider a club N with five members:

$$N = \{\text{Alan, Bill, Cathy, David, Evelyn}\},$$

or, in abbreviated form, $N = \{A, B, C, D, E\}$.

In how many ways can this group select a president (assuming all members are eligible)?

SOLUTION

The task in this case is to select one of the five members as president. There are five possible results: *A, B, C, D,* and *E*. ◼

Product Tables for Two-Part Tasks

▌ EXAMPLE 2   Building Numbers from a Set of Digits

TABLE 1

		Second Digit	
	1	**2**	**3**
First Digit **1**	11	12	13
2	21	22	23
3	31	32	33

Determine the number of two-digit numbers that can be written using digits from the set {1, 2, 3}.

SOLUTION

This task consists of two parts:

1. Choose a first digit.
2. Choose a second digit.

The results for a two-part task can be pictured in a **product table** such as Table 1. From the table we obtain our list of possible results:

$$11, 12, 13, 21, 22, 23, 31, 32, 33.$$

There are nine possibilities.

▌ EXAMPLE 3   Rolling a Pair of Dice

Determine the number of different possible results when two ordinary dice are rolled.

SOLUTION

Assume the dice are easily distinguishable. Perhaps one is red and the other green. Then the task consists of two parts:

1. Roll the red die.
2. Roll the green die.

The product table in Table 2 shows that there are thirty-six possible results.

TABLE 2   Rolling Two Fair Dice

		Green Die					
		1	**2**	**3**	**4**	**5**	**6**
Red Die	**1**	(1, 1)	(1, 2)	(1, 3)	(1, 4)	(1, 5)	(1, 6)
	2	(2, 1)	(2, 2)	(2, 3)	(2, 4)	(2, 5)	(2, 6)
	3	(3, 1)	(3, 2)	(3, 3)	(3, 4)	(3, 5)	(3, 6)
	4	(4, 1)	(4, 2)	(4, 3)	(4, 4)	(4, 5)	(4, 6)
	5	(5, 1)	(5, 2)	(5, 3)	(5, 4)	(5, 5)	(5, 6)
	6	(6, 1)	(6, 2)	(6, 3)	(6, 4)	(6, 5)	(6, 6)

You will want to refer to Table 2 when various dice-rolling problems occur in the remainder of this chapter and the next.

■ **EXAMPLE 4** **Electing Two Club Officers**

Find the number of ways that club N of Example 1 can elect both a president and a secretary. Assume that all members are eligible, but that no one can hold both offices.

SOLUTION

Again, the required task has two parts:

1. Determine the president.
2. Determine the secretary.

Constructing Table 3 gives us the possibilities (where, for example, AB denotes president A and secretary B, while BA denotes president B and secretary A).

TABLE 3		**Electing Two Officers**				
		Secretary				
		A	**B**	**C**	**D**	**E**
President	**A**		*AB*	*AC*	*AD*	*AE*
	B	*BA*		*BC*	*BD*	*BE*
	C	*CA*	*CB*		*CD*	*CE*
	D	*DA*	*DB*	*DC*		*DE*
	E	*EA*	*EB*	*EC*	*ED*	

Notice that certain entries (down the main diagonal, from upper left to lower right) are omitted from the table, since the cases *AA, BB,* and so on would imply one person holding both offices. Altogether, there are twenty possibilities. ■

■ **EXAMPLE 5** **Selecting Committees for a Club**

Find the number of ways that club N can appoint a committee of two members to represent them at an association conference.

SOLUTION

The required task again has two parts. In fact, we can refer to Table 3 again, but this time, the order of the two letters (people) in a given pair really makes no difference. For example, *BD* and *DB* are the same committee. (In Example 4, *BD* and *DB* were different results since the two people would be holding different offices.) In the case of committees, we eliminate not only the main diagonal entries, but also all entries below the main diagonal. The resulting list contains ten possibilities:

$$AB, \quad AC, \quad AD, \quad AE, \quad BC, \quad BD, \quad BE, \quad CD, \quad CE, \quad DE.$$ ■

Tree Diagrams for Multiple-Part Tasks

PROBLEM-SOLVING HINT A task that has more than two parts is not easy to analyze with a product table. Another helpful device is the **tree diagram,** which we use in the following examples.

Bone dice were unearthed in the remains of a Roman garrison, Vindolanda, near the border between England and Scotland. Life on the Roman frontier was occupied with gaming as well as fighting. Some of the Roman dice were loaded in favor of 6 and 1.

Life on the American frontier was reflected in cattle brands that were devised to keep alive the memories of hardships, feuds, and romances. A rancher named Ellis from Paradise Valley in Arizona designed his cattle brand in the shape of a pair of dice. You can guess that the pips were 6 and 1.

EXAMPLE 6   Building Numbers from a Set of Digits

Find the number of three-digit numbers that can be written using digits from the set {1, 2, 3}, assuming that **(a)** repeated digits are allowed and **(b)** repeated digits are not allowed.

SOLUTION

(a) The task of constructing such a number has three parts:

1. Select the first digit.
2. Select the second digit.
3. Select the third digit.

As we move from left to right through the tree diagram in Figure 1, the tree branches at the first stage to all possibilities for the first digit. Then each first-stage branch again branches, or splits, at the second stage, to all possibilities for the second digit. Finally, the third-stage branching shows the third-digit possibilities. The list of possible results (twenty-seven of them) is shown in Figure 1.

(b) For the case of nonrepeating digits, we could construct a whole new tree diagram, as in Figure 2, or we could simply go down the list of numbers from the first tree diagram and strike out any that contain repeated digits. In either case we obtain only six possibilities.

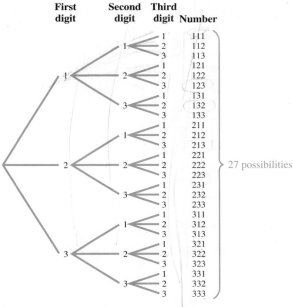

Tree diagram for three-digit numbers with digits from the set {1, 2, 3}

FIGURE 1

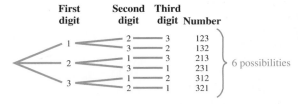

Tree diagram for nonrepeating three-digit numbers with digits from the set {1, 2, 3}

FIGURE 2

Notice the distinction between parts (a) and (b) of Example 6. There are twenty-seven possibilities when "repetitions (of digits) are allowed," but only six possibilities when "repetitions are not allowed."

Here is another way to phrase the problem of Example 6:

A three-digit number is to be determined by placing three slips of paper (marked 1, 2, and 3) into a hat and drawing out three slips in succession. Find the number of possible results if the drawing is done (**a**) *with replacement* and (**b**) *without replacement*.

Drawing "with replacement" means drawing a slip, recording its digit, and replacing the slip into the hat so that it is again available for subsequent draws. Drawing "with replacement" has the effect of "allowing repetitions," while drawing "without replacement" has the effect of "not allowing repetitions."

The words "repetitions" and "replacement" are important in the statement of a problem. In Example 2, since no restrictions were stated, we assume that *repetitions* (of digits) *are allowed,* or equivalently that digits are selected *with replacement.*

EXAMPLE 7 Selecting Switch Settings on a Printer

Michelle Clayton's computer printer allows for optional settings with a panel of four on-off switches in a row. How many different settings can she select if no two adjacent switches can both be off?

SOLUTION

This situation is typical of user-selectable options on various devices, including computer equipment, garage door openers, and other appliances. In Figure 3 we denote "on" and "off" with 1 and 0, respectively (a common practice). The number of possible settings is seen to be eight. Notice that each time on the tree diagram that a switch is indicated as off (0), the next switch can only be on (1). This is to satisfy the restriction that no two adjacent switches can both be off.

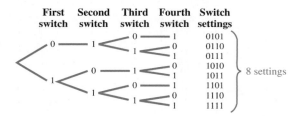

Tree diagram for printer settings

FIGURE 3

EXAMPLE 8 Seating Attendees at a Concert

Arne, Bobbette, Chuck, and Deirdre have tickets for four reserved seats in a row at a concert. In how many different ways can they seat themselves so that Arne and Bobbette will sit next to each other?

SOLUTION

Here we have a four-part task: assign people to the first, second, third, and fourth seats. The tree diagram in Figure 4 on the next page avoids repetitions, because no person can occupy more than one seat. Also, once *A* or *B* appears in the tree, the other one must occur at the next stage. (Why is this?) No splitting occurs from stage three to stage four because by that time there is only one person left unassigned. The right column in the figure shows the twelve possible seating arrangements.

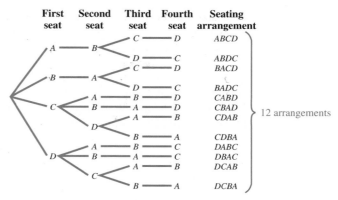

Tree diagram for concert seating

FIGURE 4

Although we have applied tree diagrams only to tasks with three or more parts, they can also be used for two-part or even simple, one-part tasks. Product tables, on the other hand, are practical only for two-part tasks.

Other Systematic Listing Methods

There are additional systematic ways to produce complete listings of possible results besides product tables and tree diagrams.

In Example 4, where we used a product table (Table 3) to list all possible president-secretary pairs for the club $N = \{A, B, C, D, E\}$, we could systematically construct the same list using a sort of alphabetical or left-to-right approach. First, consider the results where A is president. Any of the remaining members (B, C, D, or E) could then be secretary. That gives us the pairs AB, AC, AD, and AE. Next, assume B is president. The secretary could then be A, C, D, or E. We get the pairs BA, BC, BD, and BE. Continuing in order, we get the complete list just as in Example 4:

$$AB, \quad AC, \quad AD, \quad AE, \quad BA, \quad BC, \quad BD, \quad BE, \quad CA, \quad CB,$$
$$CD, \quad CE, \quad DA, \quad DB, \quad DC, \quad DE, \quad EA, \quad EB, \quad EC, \quad ED.$$

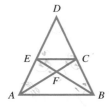

FIGURE 5

EXAMPLE 9 Counting Triangles in a Figure

How many different triangles (of any size) are included in Figure 5?

SOLUTION

One systematic approach is to label the points as shown, begin with A, and proceed in alphabetical order to write all three-letter combinations, then cross out the ones that are not triangles in the figure.

$$ABC, \quad ABD, \quad ABE, \quad ABF, \quad ACD, \quad ACE, \quad \cancel{ACF}, \quad \cancel{ADE}, \quad ADF, \quad AEF,$$
$$\cancel{BCD}, \quad BCE, \quad BCF, \quad BDE, \quad \cancel{BDF}, \quad BEF, \quad CDE, \quad \cancel{CDF}, \quad CEF, \quad \cancel{DEF}$$

Finally, there are twelve different triangles in the figure. Why are ACB and CBF (and many others) not included in the list?

Another method might be first to identify the triangles consisting of a single region each: DEC, ECF, AEF, BCF, ABF. Then list those consisting of two regions each: *AEC, BEC, ABE, ABC;* and those with three regions each: *ACD, BED.* There are no triangles with four regions, but there is one with five: *ABD.* The total is again twelve. Can you think of other systematic ways of getting the same list? ▪

Notice that in the first method shown in Example 9, the labeled points were considered in alphabetical order. In the second method, the single-region triangles were listed by using a top-to-bottom and left-to-right order. Using a definite system helps to ensure that we get a complete list.

The **"tree diagram"** on the map came from research on the feasibility of using motor-sailers (motor-driven ships with wind-sail auxiliary power) on the North Atlantic run. At the beginning of a run, weather forecasts and computer analysis are used to choose the best of the 45 million possible routes.

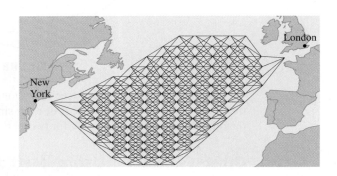

1.1 EXERCISES

Electing Officers of a Club *Refer to Examples 1 and 4, involving the club*

$$N = \{\text{Alan, Bill, Cathy, David, Evelyn}\}.$$

Assuming all members are eligible, but that no one can hold more than one office, list and count the different ways the club could elect each group of officers.

1. a president and a treasurer

2. a president and a treasurer if the president must be a female

3. a president and a treasurer if the two officers must not be the same sex

4. a president, a secretary, and a treasurer, if the president and treasurer must be women

5. a president, a secretary, and a treasurer, if the president must be a man and the other two must be women

6. a president, a secretary, and a treasurer, if the secretary must be a woman and the other two must be men

Appointing Committees *List and count the ways club N could appoint a committee of three members under each condition.*

7. There are no restrictions.

8. The committee must include more men than women.

Refer to Table 2 (the product table for rolling two dice). Of the 36 possibilities, determine the number for which the sum (for both dice) is the following.

9. 2   10. 3   11. 4

12. 5   13. 6   14. 7

15. 8   16. 9   17. 10

18. 11   19. 12   20. odd

21. even

22. from 6 through 8 inclusive

23. between 6 and 10

24. less than 5

25. Construct a product table showing all possible two-digit numbers using digits from the set

$$\{1, 2, 3, 4, 5, 6\}.$$

Of the thirty-six numbers in the product table for Exercise 25, list the ones that belong to each category.

26. odd numbers

27. numbers with repeating digits

28. multiples of 6

29. prime numbers

30. triangular numbers

31. square numbers

32. Fibonacci numbers

33. powers of 2

34. Construct a tree diagram showing all possible results when three fair coins are tossed. Then list the ways of getting each result.
(a) at least two heads
(b) more than two heads
(c) no more than two heads
(d) fewer than two heads

35. Extend the tree diagram of Exercise 34 for four fair coins. Then list the ways of getting each result.
(a) more than three tails
(b) fewer than three tails
(c) at least three tails
(d) no more than three tails

Determine the number of triangles (of any size) in each figure.

36.

37.

38.

39.

Determine the number of squares (of any size) in each figure.

40.

41.

42.

43.

Consider only the smallest individual cubes and assume solid stacks (no gaps). Determine the number of cubes in each stack that are not visible from the perspective shown.

44.

45.

46.

47.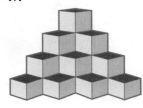

48. In the plane figure shown here, only movement that tends downward is allowed. Find the total number of paths from *A* to *B*.

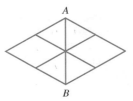

49. Find the number of paths from A to B in the figure shown here if the directions on various segments are restricted as shown.

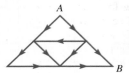

In each of Exercises 50–52, determine the number of different ways the given number can be written as the sum of two primes.

50. 30   **51.** 40   **52.** 95

53. *Shaking Hands in a Group* A group of twelve strangers sat in a circle, and each one got acquainted only with the person to the left and the person to the right. Then all twelve people stood up and each one shook hands (once) with each of the others who was still a stranger. How many handshakes occurred?

54. *Number of Games in a Chess Tournament* Fifty people enter a single-elimination chess tournament. (If you lose one game, you're out.) Assuming no ties occur, what is the number of games required to determine the tournament champion?

55. *Sums of Digits* How many of the numbers from 10 through 100 have the sum of their digits equal to a perfect square?

56. *Sums of Digits* How many three-digit numbers have the sum of their digits equal to 22?

57. *Integers Containing the Digit 2* How many integers between 100 and 400 contain the digit 2?

58. *Selecting Dinner Items* Frank Capek and friends are dining at the Bay Steamer Restaurant this evening, where a complete dinner consists of three items:
  (1) soup (clam chowder or minestrone) or salad (fresh spinach or shrimp),
  (2) sourdough rolls or bran muffin, and
  (3) entree (lasagna, lobster, or roast turkey).

Frank selects his meal subject to the following restrictions. He cannot stomach more than one kind of seafood at a sitting. Also, whenever he tastes minestrone, he cannot resist having lasagna as well. And he cannot face the teasing he would receive from his companions if he were to order both spinach and bran. Use a tree diagram to determine the number of different choices Frank has.

Setting Options on a Computer Printer *For Exercises 59–61, refer to Example 7. How many different settings could Michelle choose in each case?*

59. No restrictions apply to adjacent switches.

60. No two adjacent switches can be off *and* no two adjacent switches can be on.

61. There are five switches rather than four, and no two adjacent switches can be on.

62. *Building Numbers from Sets of Digits* Determine the number of odd, nonrepeating three-digit numbers that can be written using digits from the set {0, 1, 2, 3}.

63. *Lattice Points on a Line Segment* A line segment joins the points (8, 12) and (53, 234) in the Cartesian plane. Including its endpoints, how many lattice points does this line segment contain? (A *lattice point* is a point with integer coordinates.)

64. *Lengths of Segments Joining Lattice Points* In the pattern that follows, dots are one unit apart horizontally and vertically. If a segment can join any two dots, how many segments can be drawn with each length?
  (a) 1   **(b)** 2   **(c)** 3
  (d) 4   **(e)** 5

  • • • • •
  • • • • •
  • • • • •
  • • • • •
  • • • • •

65. *Counting Matchsticks in a Grid* Uniform-length matchsticks are used to build a rectangular grid as shown here. If the grid is 15 matchsticks high and 28 matchsticks wide, how many matchsticks are used?

66. *Patterns in Floor Tiling* A square floor is to be tiled with square tiles as shown, with blue tiles on the main diagonals and red tiles everywhere else. (In all cases, both blue and red tiles must be used and the two diagonals must have a common blue tile at the center of the floor.)

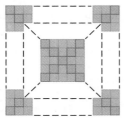

(a) If 81 blue tiles will be used, how many red tiles will be needed?

(b) For what numbers in place of 81 would this problem still be solvable?

(c) Find a formula expressing the number of red tiles required in general.

67. *Shaking Hands in a Group* Jeff Howard and his son were among four father-and-son pairs who gathered to trade baseball cards. As each person arrived, he shook hands with anyone he had not known previously. Each person ended up making a different number of new acquaintances (0–6), except Jeff and his son, who each met the same number of people. How many hands did Jeff shake?

*In Exercises 68–71, restate the given counting problem in two ways, first **(a)** using the word* repetition, *and then* **(b)** *using the word* replacement.

68. Example 2   **69.** Example 3

70. Example 4   **71.** Exercise 7

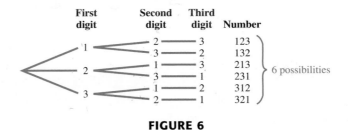

1.2 **Using the Fundamental Counting Principle**

Uniformity and the Fundamental Counting Principle • Factorials • Arrangements of Objects

Uniformity and the Fundamental Counting Principle

In Section 1.1, we obtained complete lists of all possible results for various tasks. However, if the total number of possibilities is all we need to know, then an actual listing usually is unnecessary and often is difficult or tedious to obtain, especially when the list is long. In this section, we develop ways to calculate "how many" using the *fundamental counting principle.*

Figure 6 repeats Figure 2 of Section 1.1 (for Example 6(b)) which shows all possible nonrepeating three-digit numbers with digits from the set {1, 2, 3}.

First digit	Second digit	Third digit	Number	
1	2	3	123	
1	3	2	132	
2	1	3	213	6 possibilities
2	3	1	231	
3	1	2	312	
3	2	1	321	

FIGURE 6

The tree diagram in Figure 6 is "uniform" in the sense that a given part of the task can be done in the same number of ways no matter which choices were selected for previous parts. For example, there are always two choices for the second digit. (If the first digit is 1, the second can be 2 or 3; if the first is 2, the second can be 1 or 3; if the first is 3, the second can be 1 or 2.)

Example 6(a) of Section 1.1 addressed the same basic situation: *Find the number of three-digit numbers that can be written using the digits* 1, 2, *and* 3. In that case repetitions were allowed. With repetitions allowed, there were many more possibilities (27 rather than 6—see Figure 1 of Section 1.1). But the uniformity criterion mentioned above still applied. No matter what the first digit is, there are three choices for the second (1, 2, 3). And no matter what the first and second digits are, there are three choices for the third. This uniformity criterion can be stated in general as follows.

Uniformity Criterion for Multiple-Part Tasks

A multiple-part task is said to satisfy the **uniformity criterion** if the number of choices for any particular part is the same *no matter which choices were selected for previous parts*.

The uniformity criterion is not satisfied by all multiple-part counting problems. Refer to Example 7 (and Figure 3) of Section 1.1. After the first switch (two possibilities), other switches had either one or two possible settings depending on how previous switches were set. (This "nonuniformity" arose, in that case, from the requirement that no two adjacent switches could both be off.)

In the many cases where uniformity does hold, we can avoid having to construct a tree diagram by using the **fundamental counting principle,** stated as follows.

Fundamental Counting Principle

When a task consists of k separate parts and satisfies the uniformity criterion, if the first part can be done in n_1 ways, the second part can then be done in n_2 ways, and so on through the kth part, which can be done in n_k ways, then the total number of ways to complete the task is given by the product

$$n_1 \cdot n_2 \cdot n_3 \cdot \ldots \cdot n_k.$$

PROBLEM-SOLVING HINT A problem-solving strategy: "If a formula applies, use it." The fundamental counting principle provides a formula that applies to a variety of problems. The trick is to visualize the "task" at hand as being accomplished in a sequence of two or more separate parts. A helpful technique when applying the fundamental counting principle is to write out all the separate parts of the task, with a blank for each one. Reason out how many ways each part can be done and enter these numbers in the blanks. Finally, multiply these numbers together.

Richard Dedekind (1831–1916) studied at the University of Göttingen, where he was Gauss's last student. His work was not recognized during his lifetime, but his treatment of the infinite and of what constitutes a real number are influential even today.

While on vacation in Switzerland, Dedekind met Georg Cantor. Dedekind was interested in Cantor's work on infinite sets. Perhaps because both were working in new and unusual fields of mathematics, such as number theory, and because neither received the professional attention he deserved during his lifetime, the two struck up a lasting friendship.

EXAMPLE 1   Counting the Two-Digit Numbers

How many two-digit numbers are there in our (base-ten) system of counting numbers? (While 40 is a two-digit number, 04 is not.)

SOLUTION

Our "task" here is to select, or construct, a two-digit number. We can set up the work as follows, showing the two parts to be done.

Part of task	Select first digit	Select second digit
Number of ways	_____	_____

There are nine choices for the first digit (1 through 9). Since there were no stated or implied restrictions, we assume that repetition of digits is allowed. Therefore, no matter which nonzero digit is used as the first digit, all nine choices are available for the second digit. Also, unlike the first digit, the second digit may be zero, so we have ten choices for the second digit. We can now fill in the blanks and multiply.

Part of task	Select first digit	Select second digit	
Number of ways	9 ·	10	= 90

   There are 90 two-digit numbers. (As a check, notice that they are the numbers from 10 through 99, a total of $99 - 10 + 1 = 90$.) ■

EXAMPLE 2   Building Two-Digit Numbers with Restrictions

Find the number of two-digit numbers that do not contain repeated digits.

SOLUTION

The basic task is again to select a two-digit number, and there are two parts:

1. Select the first digit.
2. Select the second digit.

But a new restriction applies—no repetition of digits. There are nine choices for the first digit (1 through 9). Then nine choices remain for the second digit, since one nonzero digit has been used and cannot be repeated, but zero is now available. The total number is $9 \cdot 9 = 81$. ■

EXAMPLE 3   Electing Club Officers with Restrictions

In how many ways can Club N of the previous section elect a president and a secretary if no one may hold more than one office and the secretary must be a man?

SOLUTION

Recall that $N = \{A, B, C, D, E\} = \{$Alan, Bill, Cathy, David, Evelyn$\}$. Considering president first, there are five choices (no restrictions). But now we have a problem with finding the number of choices for secretary. If a woman was selected president (C or E), there are three choices for secretary (A, B, and D). If a man was selected president, only two choices (the other two men) remain for secretary. In other words, the uniformity criterion is not met and our attempt to apply the fundamental counting principle has failed.

All is not lost, however. In finding the total number of ways, there is no reason we cannot consider secretary first. There are three choices (*A*, *B*, and *D*). Now, no matter which man was chosen secretary, both of the other men, and both women, are available for president (four choices in every case). In this order, we satisfy the uniformity criterion and can use the fundamental counting principle. The total number of ways to elect a president and a secretary is $3 \cdot 4 = 12$. ■

> **PROBLEM-SOLVING HINT** Example 3 suggests a useful problem-solving strategy: Whenever one or more parts of a task have special restrictions, try considering that part (or those parts) before other parts.

EXAMPLE 4 Counting Three-Digit Numbers with Restrictions

How many nonrepeating odd three-digit counting numbers are there?

SOLUTION

The most restricted digit is the third, since it must be odd. There are five choices (1, 3, 5, 7, and 9). Next, consider the first digit. It can be any nonzero digit except the one already chosen as the third digit. There are eight choices. Finally, the second digit can be any digit (including 0) except for the two (nonzero) digits already used. There are eight choices. We can summarize this reasoning as follows.

Part of task	Select third digit		Select first digit		Select second digit	
Number of ways	5	·	8	·	8	= 320

There are 320 nonrepeating odd three-digit counting numbers. ■

EXAMPLE 5 Counting License Plates

In some states, auto license plates have contained three letters followed by three digits. How many such licenses are possible?

SOLUTION

The basic task is to design a license number with three letters followed by three digits. There are six component parts to this task. Since there are no restrictions on letters or digits, the fundamental counting principle gives

$$26 \cdot 26 \cdot 26 \cdot 10 \cdot 10 \cdot 10 = 26^3 \cdot 10^3 = 17{,}576{,}000$$

possible licenses. (In practice, a few of the possible sequences of letters are considered undesirable and are not used.) ■

EXAMPLE 6 Building Numbers from a Set of Digits

A four-digit number is to be constructed using only digits from the set $\{1, 2, 3\}$.

(a) How many such numbers are possible?
(b) How many of these numbers are odd and less than 2000?

SOLUTION

(a) To construct such a number, we must select four digits, in succession, from the given set of three digits, where the selection is done with replacement (since repetition of digits is apparently allowed). By the fundamental counting principle, the number of possibilities is

$$3 \cdot 3 \cdot 3 \cdot 3 = 3^4 = 81.$$

(b) The number is less than 2000 only if the first digit is 1 (just one choice) and is odd only if the fourth digit is 1 or 3 (two choices). The second and third digits are unrestricted (three choices for each). The answer is

$$1 \cdot 3 \cdot 3 \cdot 2 = 18.$$

As a check, can you list the eighteen possibilities? ■

PROBLEM-SOLVING HINT Two of the problem-solving strategies were to "first solve a similar simpler problem," and to "look for a pattern." In fact, a problem at hand may sometimes prove to be essentially the same, or at least fit the same pattern, as another problem already solved.

EXAMPLE 7 Distributing Golf Clubs

Vern has four antique wood head golf clubs that he wants to give to his three sons, Mark, Chris, and Scott.

(a) How many ways can the clubs be distributed?
(b) How many choices are there if the power driver must go to Mark and the number 3 wood must go to either Chris or Scott?

SOLUTION

(a) The task is to distribute four clubs among three sons. Consider the clubs in succession and, for each one, ask how many sons could receive it. In effect, we must select four sons, in succession, from the set {Mark, Chris, Scott}, selecting with replacement. Compare this with Example 6(a), in which we selected four digits, in succession, from the set {1, 2, 3}, selecting with replacement. In this case, we are selecting sons rather than digits, but the pattern is the same and the numbers are the same. Again our answer is $3^4 = 81$.

(b) Just as in Example 6(b), one part of the task is now restricted to a single choice and another part is restricted to two choices. As in that example, the number of possibilities is $1 \cdot 3 \cdot 3 \cdot 2 = 18$. ◼

EXAMPLE 8 Seating Attendees at a Concert

Rework Example 8 of Section 1.1, this time using the fundamental counting principle.

SOLUTION

Recall that Arne, Bobbette, Chuck, and Deirdre (*A*, *B*, *C*, and *D*) are to seat themselves in four adjacent seats (say 1, 2, 3, and 4) so that *A* and *B* are side-by-side. One approach to accomplish this task is to make three successive decisions as follows.

1	2	3	4
X	X	_	_
_	X	X	_
_	_	X	X

Seats available to *A* and *B*

1. Which pair of seats should *A* and *B* occupy? There are *three* choices (1 and 2, 2 and 3, 3 and 4, as illustrated in the margin).
2. Which order should *A* and *B* take? There are *two* choices (*A* left of *B*, or *B* left of *A*).
3. Which order should *C* and *D* take? There are *two* choices (*C* left of *D*, or *D* left of *C*, not necessarily right next to each other).

(Why did we not ask which two seats *C* and *D* should occupy?) The fundamental counting principle now gives the total number of choices:

$$3 \cdot 2 \cdot 2 = 12 \qquad \text{Same result as in Section 1.1}$$ ◼

Factorials

Factorials This section began with a discussion of nonrepeating three-digit numbers with digits from the set {1, 2, 3}. The number of possibilities was

$$3 \cdot 2 \cdot 1 = 6,$$

in keeping with the fundamental counting principle. That product can also be thought of as the total number of distinct *arrangements* of the three digits 1, 2, and 3.

Similarly, the number of distinct arrangements of four objects, say *A, B, C,* and *D,* is, by the fundamental counting principle,

$$4 \cdot 3 \cdot 2 \cdot 1 = 24.$$

Since this type of product occurs so commonly in applications, we give it a special name and symbol as follows. For any counting number *n*, the product of *all* counting numbers from *n* down through 1 is called *n* **factorial,** and is denoted *n***!**.

Short Table of Factorials

Factorial values increase rapidly. The value of 100! is a number with 158 digits.

0!	= 1
1!	= 1
2!	= 2
3!	= 6
4!	= 24
5!	= 120
6!	= 720
7!	= 5040
8!	= 40,320
9!	= 362,880
10!	= 3,628,800

Factorial Formula

For any counting number *n*, the quantity *n* **factorial** is given by

$$n! = n(n - 1)(n - 2)\ldots 2 \cdot 1.$$

The first few factorial values are easily found by simple multiplication, but they rapidly become very large, as indicated in the margin. The use of a calculator is advised in most cases. (See the margin notes that follow.)

> **PROBLEM-SOLVING HINT** Sometimes expressions with factorials can be evaluated easily by observing that, in general, $n! = n(n - 1)!$, $n! = n(n - 1)(n - 2)!$, and so on. For example,
>
> $$8! = 8 \cdot 7!, \quad 12! = 12 \cdot 11 \cdot 10 \cdot 9!, \quad \text{and so on.}$$
>
> This pattern is especially helpful in evaluating quotients of factorials, such as
>
> $$\frac{10!}{8!} = \frac{10 \cdot 9 \cdot 8!}{8!} = 10 \cdot 9 = 90.$$

EXAMPLE 9 Evaluating Expressions Containing Factorials

Evaluate each expression.

(a) $3!$ **(b)** $6!$ **(c)** $(6 - 3)!$ **(d)** $6! - 3!$

(e) $\dfrac{6!}{3!}$ **(f)** $\left(\dfrac{6}{3}\right)!$ **(g)** $15!$ **(h)** $100!$

The results of Example 9(b), (d), and (g) are illustrated in this calculator screen.

SOLUTION

(a) $3! = 3 \cdot 2 \cdot 1 = 6$

(b) $6! = 6 \cdot 5 \cdot 4 \cdot 3 \cdot 2 \cdot 1 = 720$

(c) $(6 - 3)! = 3! = 6$

(d) $6! - 3! = 720 - 6 = 714$

(e) $\dfrac{6!}{3!} = \dfrac{6 \cdot 5 \cdot 4 \cdot 3!}{3!} = 6 \cdot 5 \cdot 4 = 120$ Note application of problem-solving hint

(f) $\left(\dfrac{6}{3}\right)! = 2! = 2 \cdot 1 = 2$

(g) $15! = 1.307674368000 \times 10^{12}$

(h) $100! = 9.332621544 \times 10^{157}$

Notice the distinction between parts (c) and (d) and between parts (e) and (f) above. Parts (g) and (h) were performed on an advanced scientific calculator. (Part (h) is beyond the capability of most scientific calculators.) ▪

So that factorials will be defined for all whole numbers, including zero, it is common to define 0! as follows.

| 0! |
| 1 |

The definition $0! = 1$ is illustrated here.

Definition of Zero Factorial

$$0! = 1$$

(We will see later that this special definition makes other results easier to state.)

Arrangements of Objects

When finding the total number of ways to *arrange* a given number of distinct objects, we can use a factorial. The fundamental counting principle would do, but factorials provide a shortcut.

Arrangements of *n* Distinct Objects

The total number of different ways to arrange *n* distinct objects is **n!**.

EXAMPLE 10 Arranging Essays

Erika Berg has seven essays to include in her English 1A folder. In how many different orders can she arrange them?

SOLUTION

The number of ways to arrange seven distinct objects is $7! = 5040$. ◼

EXAMPLE 11 Arranging Preschoolers

Lynn Damme is taking thirteen preschoolers to the park. How many ways can the children line up, in single file, to board the van?

SOLUTION

Thirteen children can be arranged in $13! = 6,227,020,800$ different ways. ◼

D₁AD₂
D₂AD₁

D₁D₂A
D₂D₁A

AD₁D₂
AD₂D₁

In counting arrangements of objects that contain look-alikes, the normal factorial formula must be modified to find the number of truly different arrangements. For example, the number of distinguishable arrangements of the letters of the word DAD is not $3! = 6$ but rather $\frac{3!}{2!} = 3$. The listing in the margin shows how the six total arrangements consist of just three groups of two, where the two in a given group look alike. In general, the distinguishable arrangements can be counted as follows.

Arrangements of *n* Objects Containing Look-Alikes

The number of **distinguishable arrangements** of *n* objects, where one or more subsets consist of look-alikes (say n_1 are of one kind, n_2 are of another kind, . . . , and n_k are of yet another kind), is given by

$$\frac{n!}{n_1!n_2!\ldots n_k!}.$$

EXAMPLE 12 Counting Distinguishable Arrangements

Determine the number of distinguishable arrangements of the letters in each word.

(a) HEEDLESS   **(b)** NOMINEE

SOLUTION

(a) For the letters of HEEDLESS, the number of distinguishable arrangements is

8 letters total ⟶ $\dfrac{8!}{3!\,2!} = 3360.$

3 E's, 2 S's ⟶

(b) For the letters of NOMINEE, the number of distinguishable arrangements is

7 letters total ⟶ $\dfrac{7!}{2!\,2!} = 1260.$

2 N's, 2 E's ⟶

For Further Thought

Stirling's Approximation for $n!$

Although all factorial values are counting numbers, they can be approximated using **Stirling's** **formula,**

$$n! \approx \sqrt{2\pi n} \cdot n^n \cdot e^{-n},$$

which involves two famous irrational numbers, π and e. For example, while the exact value of $5!$ is $5 \cdot 4 \cdot 3 \cdot 2 \cdot 1 = 120$, the corresponding approximation is

$$5! \approx \sqrt{2\pi 5} \cdot 5^5 \cdot e^{-5} \approx 118.019168,$$

which is off by less than 2, an error of only 1.65%.

For Group Discussion or Individual Investigation

Use a calculator to fill in all values in the table. The column values are defined as follows.

$C = n!$	(exact value, by calculator)
$S \approx n!$	(Stirling's approximation, by calculator)
$D =$ Difference	$(C - S)$
$P =$ Percentage difference	$\left(\dfrac{D}{C} \cdot 100\%\right)$

Try to obtain percentage differences accurate to two decimal places.

n	C	S	D	P
1				
2				
3				
4				
5				
6				
7				
8				
9				
10				

Based on your calculations, answer each question.

1. In general, is Stirling's approximation too low or too high?

2. Observe the values in the table as n grows larger.
   (a) Do the differences (D) get larger or smaller?
   (b) Do the percentage differences (P) get larger or smaller?
   (c) Does Stirling's formula become more accurate or less accurate?

1.2 EXERCISES

1. Explain the fundamental counting principle in your own words.

2. Describe how factorials can be used in counting problems.

For Exercises 3–6, n and m are counting numbers. Do the following: **(a)** *Tell whether the given statement is true in general, and* **(b)** *explain your answer, using specific examples.*

3. $(n + m)! = n! + m!$

4. $(n \cdot m)! = n! \cdot m!$

5. $(n - m)! = n! - m!$

6. $n! = n(n - 1)!$

Evaluate each expression without using a calculator.

7. 4!

8. 7!

9. $\dfrac{8!}{5!}$

10. $\dfrac{16!}{14!}$

11. $\dfrac{5!}{(5-2)!}$

12. $\dfrac{6!}{(6-4)!}$

13. $\dfrac{9!}{6!(6-3)!}$

14. $\dfrac{10!}{4!(10-4)!}$

15. $\dfrac{n!}{(n-r)!}$, where $n = 7$ and $r = 4$

16. $\dfrac{n!}{r!(n-r)!}$, where $n = 12$ and $r = 4$

Evaluate each expression using a calculator. (Some answers may not be exact.)

17. 11!

18. 17!

19. $\dfrac{12!}{7!}$

20. $\dfrac{15!}{9!}$

21. $\dfrac{13!}{(13-3)!}$

22. $\dfrac{16!}{(16-6)!}$

23. $\dfrac{20!}{10! \cdot 10!}$

24. $\dfrac{18!}{6! \cdot 12!}$

25. $\dfrac{n!}{(n-r)!}$, where $n = 23$ and $r = 10$

26. $\dfrac{n!}{r!(n-r)!}$, where $n = 28$ and $r = 15$

Arranging Letters *Find the number of distinguishable arrangements of the letters of each word.*

27. SYNDICATE

28. GOOGOL

29. NONSENSE

30. HEEBIE-JEEBIES

Settings on a Switch Panel *A panel containing three on–off switches in a row is to be set.*

31. Assuming no restrictions on individual switches, use the fundamental counting principle to find the total number of possible panel settings.

32. Assuming no restrictions, construct a tree diagram to list all the possible panel settings of Exercise 31.

33. Now assume that no two adjacent switches can both be off. Explain why the fundamental counting principle does not apply.

34. Construct a tree diagram to list all possible panel settings under the restriction of Exercise 33.

35. ***Rolling Dice*** Table 2 in the previous section shows that there are 36 possible outcomes when two fair dice are rolled. How many would there be if three fair dice were rolled?

36. ***Counting Five-Digit Numbers*** How many five-digit numbers are there in our system of counting numbers?

Matching Club Members with Tasks *Recall the club*

$$N = \{\text{Alan, Bill, Cathy, David, Evelyn}\}.$$

In how many ways could they do each of the following?

37. line up all five members for a photograph

38. schedule one member to work in the office on each of five different days, assuming members may work more than one day

39. select a male and a female to decorate for a party

40. select two members, one to open their next meeting and another to close it, given that Bill will not be present

Building Numbers from Sets of Digits *In Exercises 41–44, counting numbers are to be formed using only digits from the set $\{3, 4, 5\}$. Determine the number of different possibilities for each type of number described.*

41. two-digit numbers

42. odd three-digit numbers

43. four-digit numbers with one pair of adjacent 4s and no other repeated digits (*Hint:* You may want to split the task of designing such a number into three parts, such as *(1)* position the pair of 4s, *(2)* position the 3, and *(3)* position the 5.)

44. five-digit numbers beginning and ending with 3 and with unlimited repetitions allowed

Selecting Dinner Items The Casa Loma Restaurant offers four choices in the soup and salad category (two soups and two salads), two choices in the bread category, and three choices in the entree category. Find the number of dinners available in each case.

45. One item is to be included from each of the three categories.

46. Only soup and entree are to be included.

Selecting Answers on a Test Determine the number of possible ways to mark your answer sheet (with an answer for each question) for each test.

47. a six-question true-or-false test

48. a twenty-question multiple-choice test with five answer choices for each question

Selecting a College Class Schedule Tiffany Connolly's class schedule for next semester must consist of exactly one class from each of the four categories shown.

Category	Choices	Number of Choices
English	Medieval Literature Composition Modern Poetry	3
Mathematics	History of Mathematics College Algebra Finite Mathematics	3
Computer Information Science	Introduction to Spreadsheets Advanced Word Processing C Programming BASIC Programming	4
Sociology	Social Problems Sociology of the Middle East Aging in America Minorities in America Women in American Culture	5

For each situation in Exercises 49–54, use the table at the bottom of the left column to determine the number of different sets of classes Tiffany can take.

49. All classes shown are available.

50. She is not eligible for Modern Poetry or for C Programming.

51. All sections of Minorities in America and Women in American Culture already are filled.

52. She does not have the prerequisites for Medieval Literature, Finite Mathematics, or C Programming.

53. Funding has been withdrawn for three of the computer courses and for two of the Sociology courses.

54. She must complete English Composition and Aging in America next semester to fulfill her degree requirements.

55. *Selecting Clothing* Sean took two pairs of shoes, five pairs of pants, and six shirts on a trip. Assuming all items are compatible, how many different outfits can he wear?

56. *Selecting Music Equipment* A music equipment outlet stocks ten different guitars, four guitar cases, six amplifiers, and three effects processors, with all items mutually compatible and all suitable for beginners. How many different complete setups could Lionel choose to start his musical career?

57. *Counting ZIP Codes* Tonya's ZIP code is 85726. How many ZIP codes, altogether, could be formed, each one using those same five digits?

58. *Listing Phone Numbers* John Cross keeps the phone numbers for his seven closest friends (three men and four women) in his digital phone memory. How many ways can he list them if
(a) men are listed before women?
(b) men are all listed together?
(c) no two men are listed next to each other?

Seating Arrangements at a Theater Arne, Bobbette, Chuck, Deirdre, Ed, and Fran have reserved six seats in a row at the theater, starting at an aisle seat. (Refer to Example 8 in this section.)

59. In how many ways can they arrange themselves? (*Hint:* Divide the task into the series of six parts shown below, performed in order.)
(a) If *A* is seated first, how many seats are available for him?
(b) Now, how many are available for *B*?

(c) Now, how many for C?

(d) Now, how many for D?

(e) Now, how many for E?

(f) Now, how many for F?

Now multiply together your six answers above.

60. In how many ways can they arrange themselves so that Arne and Bobbette will be next to each other?

1	2	3	4	5	6
X	X	_	_	_	_
_	X	X	_	_	_
_	_	X	X	_	_
_	_	_	X	X	_
_	_	_	_	X	X

Seats available to A and B

(*Hint:* First answer the following series of questions, assuming these parts are to be accomplished in order.)

(a) How many pairs of adjacent seats can A and B occupy?

(b) Now, given the two seats for A and B, in how many orders can they be seated?

(c) Now, how many seats are available for C?

(d) Now, how many for D?

(e) Now, how many for E?

(f) Now, how many for F?

Now multiply your six answers above.

61. In how many ways can they arrange themselves if the men and women are to alternate seats and a man must sit on the aisle? (*Hint:* First answer the following series of questions.)

(a) How many choices are there for the person to occupy the first seat, next to the aisle? (It must be a man.)

(b) Now, how many choices of people may occupy the second seat from the aisle? (It must be a woman.)

(c) Now, how many for the third seat? (one of the remaining men)

(d) Now, how many for the fourth seat? (a woman)

(e) Now, how many for the fifth seat? (a man)

(f) Now, how many for the sixth seat? (a woman)

Now multiply your six answers above.

62. In how many ways can they arrange themselves if the men and women are to alternate with either a man or a woman on the aisle? (*Hint:* First answer the following series of questions.)

(a) How many choices of people are there for the aisle seat?

(b) Now, how many are there for the second seat? (This person may not be of the same sex as the person on the aisle.)

(c) Now, how many choices are there for the third seat?

(d) Now, how many for the fourth seat?

(e) Now, how many for the fifth seat?

(f) Now, how many for the sixth seat?

Now multiply your six answers above.

63. Try working Example 4 by considering digits in the order first, then second, then third. Explain what goes wrong.

64. Try working Example 4 by considering digits in the order third, then second, then first. Explain what goes wrong.

65. Repeat Example 4 but this time allow repeated digits. Does the order in which digits are considered matter in this case?

1.3 | Using Permutations and Combinations

Permutations • Combinations • Guidelines on Which Method to Use

Permutations In Section 1.2 we introduced factorials as a way of counting the number of *arrangements* of a given set of objects. For example, the members of the club

$$N = \{\text{Alan, Bill, Cathy, David, Evelyn}\}$$

can arrange themselves in a row for a photograph in 5! = 120 different ways. We have also used previous methods, like tree diagrams and the fundamental counting principle, to answer questions such as: How many ways can club N elect a president, a secretary, and a treasurer if no one person can hold more than one office? This again is a matter of *arrangements*. The difference is that only three, rather than all five, of the members are involved in each arrangement. A common way to rephrase the basic question here is as follows:

How many arrangements are there of five things taken three at a time?

The answer, by the fundamental counting principle, is $5 \cdot 4 \cdot 3 = 60$. The factors begin with 5 and proceed downward, just as in a factorial product, but do not go all the way to 1. (In this example the product stops when there are three factors.) We now generalize this idea.

In the context of counting problems, arrangements are often called **permutations;** the number of permutations of n distinct things taken r at a time is denoted ${}_nP_r$.* Since the number of objects being arranged cannot exceed the total number available, we assume for our purposes here that $r \leq n$. Applying the fundamental counting principle to arrangements of this type gives

$${}_nP_r = n(n-1)(n-2)\ldots[n-(r-1)].$$

Notice that the first factor is $n - 0$, the second is $n - 1$, the third is $n - 2$, and so on. The rth factor, the last one in the product, will be the one with $r - 1$ subtracted from n, as shown above. We can express permutations, in general, in terms of factorials, and obtain a practical formula for calculation as follows.

$$
\begin{aligned}
{}_nP_r &= n(n-1)(n-2)\ldots[n-(r-1)] \\
&= n(n-1)(n-2)\ldots(n-r+1) \qquad \text{Simplify the last factor.} \\
&= \frac{n(n-1)(n-2)\ldots(n-r+1)(n-r)(n-r-1)\ldots 2 \cdot 1}{(n-r)(n-r-1)\ldots 2 \cdot 1} \qquad \begin{array}{l}\text{Multiply and divide by}\\ (n-r)(n-r-1)\ldots 2 \cdot 1.\end{array}\\
&= \frac{n!}{(n-r)!} \qquad \text{Definition of factorial}
\end{aligned}
$$

We summarize as follows.

Factorial Formula for Permutations

The number of **permutations,** or *arrangements,* of n distinct things taken r at a time, where $r \leq n$, can be calculated as

$$ {}_nP_r = \frac{n!}{(n-r)!}. $$

Note that although we sometimes refer to a symbol such as ${}_4P_2$ as "a permutation"(see Examples 1 and 2), the symbol actually represents "the number of permutations of 4 distinct things taken 2 at a time."

---

*Alternative notations are $P(n, r)$ and P_r^n.

EXAMPLE 1 Using the Factorial Formula for Permutations

Evaluate each permutation.

(a) $_4P_2$ (b) $_8P_5$ (c) $_5P_5$

```
4!/(4-2)!
              12
8!/(8-5)!
            6720
5!/(5-5)!
             120
```

This screen uses factorials to support the results of Example 1.

SOLUTION

(a) $_4P_2 = \dfrac{4!}{(4-2)!} = \dfrac{4!}{2!} = \dfrac{24}{2} = 12$

(b) $_8P_5 = \dfrac{8!}{(8-5)!} = \dfrac{8!}{3!} = \dfrac{40,320}{6} = 6720$

(c) $_5P_5 = \dfrac{5!}{(5-5)!} = \dfrac{5!}{0!} = \dfrac{120}{1} = 120$ ◼

Notice that $_5P_5$ is equal to 5!. It is true for all whole numbers n that

$$_nP_n = n!.$$

(This is the number of possible arrangements of n distinct objects taken all n at a time.)

Most graphing and scientific calculators allow direct calculation of permutations, in which case the factorial formula is not needed.

```
10 nPr 6
          151200
28 nPr 0
               1
18 nPr 12
   8.892185702E12
```

This screen uses the permutations feature to support the results of Example 2.

EXAMPLE 2 Calculating Permutations Directly

Evaluate each permutation.

(a) $_{10}P_6$ (b) $_{28}P_0$ (c) $_{18}P_{12}$

SOLUTION

(a) $_{10}P_6 = 151,200$ (b) $_{28}P_0 = 1$

(c) $_{18}P_{12} = 8,892,185,702,400$ ◼

Concerning part (c), many calculators will not display this many digits, so you may obtain an answer such as 8.8921857×10^{12}.

PROBLEM-SOLVING HINT Permutations can be used any time we need to know the number of size-r arrangements that can be selected from a size-n set. The word *arrangement* implies an ordering, so we use permutations only in cases when

1. repetitions are not allowed, and
2. **order is important.**

Change ringing, the English way of ringing church bells, combines mathematics and music. Bells are rung first in sequence, 1, 2, 3, ... Then the sequence is permuted ("changed"). On six bells, 720 different "changes" (different permutations of tone) can be rung: $_6P_6 = 6!$.

Composers work out changes so that musically interesting and harmonious sequences occur regularly.

The church bells are swung by means of ropes attached to the wheels beside them. One ringer swings each bell, listening intently and watching the other ringers closely. If one ringer gets lost and stays lost, the rhythm of the ringing cannot be maintained; all the ringers have to stop.

A ringer can spend weeks just learning to keep a bell going and months learning to make the bell ring in exactly the right place. Errors of $\frac{1}{4}$ second mean that two bells are ringing at the same time. Even errors of $\frac{1}{10}$ second can be heard.

■ **EXAMPLE 3   Building Numbers from a Set of Digits**

How many nonrepeating three-digit numbers can be written using digits from the set {3, 4, 5, 6, 7, 8}?

SOLUTION

Repetitions are not allowed since the numbers are to be "nonrepeating." (For example, 448 is not acceptable.) Also, order is important. (For example, 476 and 746 are *distinct* cases.) So we use permutations:

$$_6P_3 = 6 \cdot 5 \cdot 4 = 120.$$ ■

The next example involves multiple parts, and hence calls for the fundamental counting principle, but the individual parts can be handled with permutations.

■ **EXAMPLE 4   Designing Account Numbers**

Suppose certain account numbers are to consist of two letters followed by four digits and then three more letters, where repetitions of letters or digits are not allowed *within* any of the three groups, but the last group of letters may contain one or both of those used in the first group. How many such accounts are possible?

SOLUTION

The task of designing such a number consists of three parts:

1. Determine the first set of two letters.
2. Determine the set of four digits.
3. Determine the final set of three letters.

Each part requires an arrangement without repetitions, which is a permutation. Multiply together the results of the three parts.

$$_{26}P_2 \cdot {}_{10}P_4 \cdot {}_{26}P_3 = \underbrace{650}_{\text{Part 1}} \cdot \underbrace{5040}_{\text{Part 2}} \cdot \underbrace{15,600}_{\text{Part 3}}$$
$$= 51,105,600,000$$ ■

Combinations We introduced permutations to evaluate the number of arrangements of n things taken r at a time, where repetitions are not allowed. The order of the items was important. Recall that club

$$N = \{\text{Alan, Bill, Cathy, David, Evelyn}\}$$

could elect three officers in $_5P_3 = 60$ different ways. With three-member committees, on the other hand, order is not important. The committees B, D, E and E, B, D are not different. The possible number of committees is not the number of arrangements of size 3. Rather, it is the number of *subsets* of size 3 (since the order of elements in a set makes no difference).

Subsets in this new context are called **combinations.** The number of combinations of n things taken r at a time (that is, the number of size r subsets, given a set of size n) is written $_nC_r$.* Since there are n things available and we are choosing r of them, we can read $_nC_r$ as "n choose r."

The size-3 committees (subsets) of the club (set) $N = \{A, B, C, D, E\}$ are:

$$\{A, B, C\}, \quad \{A, B, D\}, \quad \{A, B, E\}, \quad \{A, C, D\}, \quad \{A, C, E\},$$
$$\{A, D, E\}, \quad \{B, C, D\}, \quad \{B, C, E\}, \quad \{B, D, E\}, \quad \{C, D, E\}.$$

There are ten subsets of size 3, so ten is the number of three-member committees possible. Just as with permutations, repetitions are not allowed. For example, $\{E, E, B\}$ is not a valid three-member subset, just as EEB is not a valid three-member arrangement.

To see how to find the number of such subsets without listing them all, notice that each size-3 subset (combination) gives rise to six size-3 arrangements (permutations). For example, the single combination ADE yields these six permutations:

$$A, D, E \quad A, E, D \quad D, A, E \quad D, E, A \quad E, A, D \quad E, D, A.$$

There must be six times as many size-3 permutations as there are size-3 combinations, or, in other words, one-sixth as many combinations as permutations. Therefore,

$$_5C_3 = \frac{_5P_3}{6} = \frac{60}{6} = 10.$$

Again, the 6 appears in the denominator because there are six different ways to arrange a set of three things (since $3! = 3 \cdot 2 \cdot 1 = 6$). Generalizing from this example, we can obtain a formula for evaluating numbers of combinations.

$$_nC_r = \frac{_nP_r}{r!} \qquad \text{\small r things can be arranged in $r!$ ways.}$$

$$= \frac{\dfrac{n!}{(n-r)!}}{r!} \qquad \text{\small Substitute the factorial formula for $_nP_r$.}$$

$$= \frac{n!}{r!(n-r)!}. \qquad \text{\small Simplify algebraically.}$$

We summarize as follows.

"Bilateral cipher" (above) was invented by **Francis Bacon** early in the seventeenth century to code political secrets. This binary code, *a* and *b* in combinations of five, has 32 permutations. Bacon's "biformed alphabet" (bottom four rows) uses two type fonts to conceal a message in some straight text. The decoder deciphers a string of *a*s and *b*s, groups them by fives, then deciphers letters and words. This code was applied to Shakespeare's plays in efforts to prove Bacon the rightful author.

Factorial Formula for Combinations

The number of **combinations,** or *subsets,* of n distinct things taken r at a time, where $r \leq n$, can be calculated as

$$_nC_r = \frac{_nP_r}{r!} = \frac{n!}{r!(n-r)!}.$$

---

*Alternative notations are $C(n, r)$, C_r^n, and $\binom{n}{r}$.

In Examples 5 and 6, you will again note the "shorthand" terminology whereby we refer to $_nC_r$ as "a combination" even though it actually represents "the number of combinations of n distinct things taken r at a time."

EXAMPLE 5 Using the Factorial Formula for Combinations

```
9!/(7!*2!)
              36
24!/(18!*6!)
           134596
```

This screen uses factorials to support the results of Example 5.

Evaluate each combination.

(a) $_9C_7$ **(b)** $_{24}C_{18}$

SOLUTION

(a) $_9C_7 = \dfrac{9!}{7!(9-7)!} = \dfrac{9!}{7!2!} = \dfrac{362,880}{5040 \cdot 2} = 36$

(b) $_{24}C_{18} = \dfrac{24!}{18!(24-18)!} = \dfrac{24!}{18!6!} = 134,596$ ■

A calculator that does permutations directly likely will do combinations directly as well. We illustrate in Example 6.

```
14 nCr 6
            3003
21 nCr 15
           54264
```

This screen uses the combinations feature to support the results of Example 6.

EXAMPLE 6 Calculating Combinations Directly

Evaluate each combination.

(a) $_{14}C_6$ **(b)** $_{21}C_{15}$

SOLUTION

(a) $_{14}C_6 = 3003$ **(b)** $_{21}C_{15} = 54,264$ ■

PROBLEM-SOLVING HINT Combinations have an important common property with permutations (repetitions are not allowed) and also have an important distinction (order is *not* important with combinations). Combinations are applied only when

1. repetitions are not allowed, and
2. **order is *not* important.**

EXAMPLE 7 Finding the Number of Subsets

Find the number of different subsets of size 2 in the set $\{a, b, c, d\}$. List them to check the answer.

SOLUTION

A subset of size 2 must have two distinct elements, so repetitions are not allowed. And since the order in which the elements of a set are listed makes no difference, we see that order is not important. Use the combinations formula with $n = 4$ and $r = 2$.

$$_4C_2 = \frac{4!}{2!(4-2)!} = \frac{4!}{2!\,2!} = 6$$

The six subsets of size 2 are $\{a, b\}, \{a, c\}, \{a, d\}, \{b, c\}, \{b, d\}, \{c, d\}$.

The set of 52 playing cards in the standard deck has four suits.

  ♠ spades   ♦ diamonds
  ♥ hearts   ♣ clubs

Ace is the unit card. Jacks, queens, and kings are "face cards." Each suit contains thirteen denominations: ace, 2, 3, . . . , 10, jack, queen, king. (In some games, ace rates above king, instead of counting as 1.)

EXAMPLE 8 Finding the Number of Possible Poker Hands

A common form of poker involves hands (sets) of five cards each, dealt from a standard deck consisting of 52 different cards (illustrated in the margin). How many different 5-card hands are possible?

SOLUTION

A 5-card hand must contain five distinct cards, so repetitions are not allowed. Also, the order is not important since a given hand depends only on the cards it contains, and not on the order in which they were dealt or the order in which they are displayed. Since order does not matter, use combinations (and a calculator):

$$_{52}C_5 = \frac{52!}{5!(52-5)!} = \frac{52!}{5!\,47!} = 2{,}598{,}960.$$

EXAMPLE 9 Finding the Number of Subsets of Books

Melvin wants to buy ten different books but can afford only four of them. In how many ways can he make his selections?

SOLUTION

The four books selected must be distinct (repetitions are not allowed), and also the order of the four chosen has no bearing in this case, so we use combinations:

$$_{10}C_4 = \frac{10!}{4!(10-4)!} = \frac{10!}{4!\,6!} = 210 \text{ ways.}$$

Notice that, according to our formula for combinations,

$$_{10}C_6 = \frac{10!}{6!(10-6)!} = \frac{10!}{6!\,4!} = 210,$$

which is the same as $_{10}C_4$. In fact, Exercise 58 asks you to prove the fact that, in general, for all whole numbers n and r, with $r \le n$,

$$_nC_r = {}_nC_{n-r}.$$

See the margin note as well. It indicates that $_{10}C_6$ is equal to $_{10}C_4$.

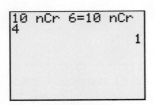

The "1" indicates that the statement

$$_{10}C_6 = {}_{10}C_4$$

is true.

Guidelines on Which Method to Use

Both permutations and combinations produce the number of ways of selecting r items from n items where repetitions are not allowed. Permutations apply to arrangements (where order is important), while combinations apply to subsets (where order is not important). These similarities and differences, as well as the appropriate formulas, are summarized in the following table.

Permutations	**Combinations**
Number of ways of selecting r items out of n items	
Repetitions are not allowed.	
Order is important.	Order is not important.
Arrangements of n items taken r at a time	Subsets of n items taken r at a time
$$_nP_r = \frac{n!}{(n-r)!}$$	$$_nC_r = \frac{n!}{r!(n-r)!}$$
Clue words: arrangement, schedule, order	Clue words: set, group, sample, selection

In cases where r items are to be selected from n items and repetitions *are* allowed, it is usually best to make direct use of the fundamental counting principle.

PROBLEM-SOLVING HINT   Many counting problems involve selecting some of the items from a given set of items. The particular conditions of the problem will determine which specific technique to use. The following guidelines may help.

1. **If selected items can be repeated, use the fundamental counting principle.**
   Example: How many four-digit numbers are there?
   $$9 \cdot 10^3 = 9000$$

2. **If selected items cannot be repeated, and order is important, use permutations.**
   Example: How many ways can three of eight people line up at a ticket counter?
   $$_8P_3 = \frac{8!}{(8-3)!} = 336$$

3. **If selected items cannot be repeated, and order is *not* important, use combinations.**
   Example: How many ways can a committee of three be selected from a group of twelve people?
   $$_{12}C_3 = \frac{12!}{3!(12-3)!} = 220$$

EXAMPLE 10   Distributing Toys to Children

In how many ways can a mother distribute three different toys among her seven children if a child may receive anywhere from none to all three toys?

SOLUTION

Because a given child can be a repeat recipient, repetitions are allowed here, so we use the fundamental counting principle. Each of the three toys can go to any of the seven children. The number of possible distributions is $7 \cdot 7 \cdot 7 = 343$. ∎

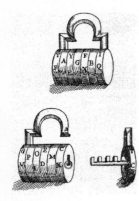

The illustration above is from the 1560s text ***Logistica***, by the mathematician J. Buteo. Among other topics, the book discusses the number of possible throws of four dice and the number of arrangements of the cylinders of a combination lock. Note that "combination" is a misleading name for these locks since repetitions are allowed, and, also, order makes a difference.

EXAMPLE 11   Selecting Committees

How many different three-member committees could club N appoint so that exactly one woman is on the committee?

SOLUTION

Recall that $N = \{$Alan, Bill, Cathy, David, Evelyn$\}$. Two members are women; three are men. Although the question mentioned only that the committee must include exactly one woman, in order to complete the committee two men must be selected as well. Therefore the task of selecting the committee members consists of two parts:

1. Choose one woman.
2. Choose two men.

Because order is not important for committees, use combinations for the two parts. One woman can be chosen in $_2C_1 = \frac{2!}{1!\,1!} = 2$ ways, and two men can be chosen in $_3C_2 = \frac{3!}{2!\,1!} = 3$ ways. Finally, use the fundamental counting principle to obtain $2 \cdot 3 = 6$ different committees. This small number can be checked by listing.

$$\{C, A, B\}, \{C, A, D\}, \{C, B, D\}, \{E, A, B\}, \{E, A, D\}, \{E, B, D\}.$$

EXAMPLE 12   Selecting Attendees for an Event

Every member of the Alpha Beta Gamma fraternity would like to attend a special event this weekend, but only ten members will be allowed to attend. How many ways could the lucky ten be selected if there are a total of forty-eight members?

SOLUTION

In this case, ten distinct men are required (repetitions are not allowed), and the order of selection makes no difference, so we use combinations.

$$_{48}C_{10} = \frac{48!}{10!\,38!} = 6{,}540{,}715{,}896 \quad \text{Use a calculator.}$$

EXAMPLE 13   Selecting Escorts

When the ten fraternity men of Example 12 arrive at the event, four of them are selected to escort the four homecoming queen candidates. In how many ways can this selection be made?

SOLUTION

Of the ten, four distinct men are required, and order is important here because different orders will pair the men with different women. Use permutations to obtain

$$_{10}P_4 = \frac{10!}{6!} = 5040 \text{ possible selections.}$$

Most, if not all, of the exercises in this section will call for permutations and/or combinations. And in the case of multiple-part tasks, the fundamental counting principle may also be required.

For Further Thought

Poker Hands

In 5-card poker, played with a standard 52-card deck, 2,598,960 different hands are possible. (See Example 8.) The desirability of the various hands depends upon their relative chance of occurrence, which, in turn, depends on the number of different ways they can occur, as shown in Table 4. Note that an ace can generally be positioned either below 2 (as a 1) or above king (as a 14). This is important in counting straight flush hands and straight hands.

TABLE 4 Categories of Hands in 5-Card Poker

Event E	Description of Event E	Number of Outcomes Favorable to E
Royal flush	Ace, king, queen, jack, and 10, all of the same suit	4
Straight flush	5 cards of consecutive denominations, all in the same suit (excluding royal flush)	36
Four of a kind	4 cards of the same denomination, plus 1 additional card	_____
Full house	3 cards of one denomination, plus 2 cards of a second denomination	3744
Flush	Any 5 cards all of the same suit (excluding royal flush and straight flush)	_____
Straight	5 cards of consecutive denominations (not all the same suit)	10,200
Three of a kind	3 cards of one denomination, plus 2 cards of two additional denominations	54,912
Two pairs	2 cards of one denomination, plus 2 cards of a second denomination, plus 1 card of a third denomination	_____
One pair	2 cards of one denomination, plus 3 additional cards of three different denominations	1,098,240
No pair	No two cards of the same denomination (and excluding any sort of flush or straight)	1,302,540
Total		**2,598,960**

For Group Discussion or Individual Investigation

As the table shows, a full house is a relatively rare occurrence. (Only four of a kind, straight flush, and royal flush are less likely.) To verify that there are 3744 different full house hands possible, carry out the following steps.

1. Explain why there are $_4C_3$ different ways to select three aces from the deck.

2. Explain why there are $_4C_2$ different ways to select two 8s from the deck.

3. If "aces and 8s" (three aces and two 8s) is one kind of full house, show that there are $_{13}P_2$ different kinds of full house altogether.

4. Multiply the expressions from Steps 1, 2, and 3 together. Explain why this product should give the total number of full house hands possible.

5. Find the three missing values in the right column of Table 4. (Answers are on page 57.)

1.3 EXERCISES

Evaluate each expression.

1. $_7P_4$

2. $_{14}P_5$

3. $_{12}C_4$

4. $_{15}C_9$

Determine the number of permutations (arrangements) of each of the following.

5. 18 things taken 5 at a time

6. 12 things taken 7 at a time

Determine the number of combinations (subsets) of each of the following.

7. 8 things taken 4 at a time

8. 14 things taken 5 at a time

Use a calculator to evaluate each expression.

9. $_{22}P_9$

10. $_{33}C_{11}$

11. Is it possible to evaluate $_6P_{10}$? Explain.

12. Is it possible to evaluate $_9C_{12}$? Explain.

13. Explain how permutations and combinations differ.

14. Explain how factorials are related to permutations.

15. Decide whether each object is a permutation or a combination.
  (a) a telephone number
  (b) a Social Security number
  (c) a hand of cards in poker
  (d) a committee of politicians
  (e) the "combination" on a student gym locker combination lock
  (f) a lottery choice of six numbers where the order does not matter
  (g) an automobile license plate number

Exercises 16–23 can be solved with permutations even though the problem statements will not always include a form of the word "permutation," or "arrangement," or "ordering."

16. *Placing in a Race* How many different ways could first-, second-, and third-place finishers occur in a race with six runners competing?

17. *Arranging New Home Models* Jeff Hubbard, a contractor, builds homes of eight different models and presently has five lots to build on. In how many different ways can he arrange homes on these lots? Assume five different models will be built.

18. *ATM PIN Numbers* An automated teller machine (ATM) requires a four-digit personal identification number (PIN), using the digits 0–9. (The first digit may be 0.) How many such PINs have no repeated digits?

19. *Electing Officers of a Club* How many ways can president and vice president be determined in a club with twelve members?

20. *Counting Prize Winners* First, second, and third prizes are to be awarded to three different people. If there are ten eligible candidates, how many outcomes are possible?

21. *Counting Prize Winners* How many ways can a teacher give five different prizes to five of her 25 students?

22. *Scheduling Security Team Visits* A security team visits 12 offices each night. How many different ways can the team order its visits?

23. *Sums of Digits* How many counting numbers have four distinct nonzero digits such that the sum of the four digits is
  (a) 10?   **(b)** 11?

Exercises 24–31 can be solved with combinations even though the problem statements will not always include the word "combination" or "subset."

24. *Sampling Cell Phones* How many ways can a sample of five cell phones be selected from a shipment of twenty-four cell phones?

25. **Detecting Defective Cell Phones** If the shipment of Exercise 24 contains six defective phones, how many of the size-five samples would not include any of the defective ones?

26. **Committees of U.S. Senators** How many different five-member committees could be formed from the 100 U.S. senators?

27. **Selecting Hands of Cards** Refer to the standard 52-card deck pictured on page 28 and notice that the deck contains four aces, twelve face cards, thirteen hearts (all red), thirteen diamonds (all red), thirteen spades (all black), and thirteen clubs (all black). Of the 2,598,960 different five-card hands possible, decide how many would consist of the following cards.
   (a) all diamonds
   (b) all black cards
   (c) all aces

28. **Selecting Lottery Entries** In a $\frac{7}{39}$ lottery, you select seven distinct numbers from the set 1 through 39, where order makes no difference. How many different ways can you make your selection?

29. **Arranging New Home Models** Jeff Hubbard (the contractor) is to build six homes on a block in a new subdivision. Overhead expenses have forced him to limit his line to two different models, standard and deluxe. (All standard model homes are the same and all deluxe model homes are the same.)
   (a) How many different choices does Jeff have in positioning the six houses if he decides to build three standard and three deluxe models?
   (b) If Jeff builds only two deluxes and four standards, how many different positionings can he use?

30. **Choosing a Monogram** Judy Zahrndt wants to name her new baby so that his monogram (first, middle, and last initials) will be distinct letters in alphabetical order and he will share her last name. How many different monograms could she select?

31. **Number of Paths from Point to Point** How many paths are possible from A to B if all motion must be to the right or downward? (*Hint:* It takes ten unit steps to get from A to B and three of the ten must be downward.)

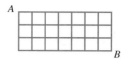

For Exercises 32–56, you may use permutations, combinations, the fundamental counting principle, or other counting methods as appropriate. (Some problems may require using more than one method.)

32. **Selecting Lottery Entries** In SuperLotto Plus, a California state lottery game, you select five distinct numbers from 1 to 47, and one MEGA number from 1 to 27, hoping that your selection will match a random list selected by lottery officials.
   (a) How many different sets of six numbers can you select?
   (b) Eileen Burke always includes her age and her husband's age as two of the first five numbers in her SuperLotto Plus selections. How many ways can she complete her list of six numbers?

33. **Drawing Cards** How many cards must be drawn (without replacement) from a standard deck of 52 to guarantee the following?
   (a) Two of the cards will be of the same suit.
   (b) Three of the cards will be of the same suit.

34. **Flush Hands in Poker** How many different 5-card poker hands would contain only cards of a single suit?

35. **Identification Numbers in Research** Subject identification numbers in a certain scientific research project consist of three letters followed by three digits and then three more letters. Assume repetitions are not allowed within any of the three groups, but letters in the first group of three may occur also in the last group of three. How many distinct identification numbers are possible?

36. **Radio Station Call Letters** Radio stations in the United States have call letters that begin with K or W (for west or east of the Mississippi River, respectively). Some have three call letters, such as WBZ in Boston, WLS in Chicago, and KGO in San Francisco. Assuming no repetition of letters, how many three-letter sets of call letters are possible?

37. *Radio Station Call Letters* Most stations that were licensed after 1927 have four call letters starting with K or W, such as WXYZ in Detroit or KRLD in Dallas. Assuming no repetitions, how many four-letter sets are possible?

38. *Scheduling Games in a Basketball League* Each team in an eight-team basketball league is scheduled to play each other team three times. How many games will be played altogether?

39. *Scheduling Batting Orders in Baseball* The Coyotes, a youth league baseball team, have seven pitchers, who only pitch, and twelve other players, all of whom can play any position other than pitcher. For Saturday's game, the coach has not yet determined which nine players to use nor what the batting order will be, except that the pitcher will bat last. How many different batting orders may occur?

40. *Ordering Performers in a Music Recital* A music class of eight girls and seven boys is having a recital. If each member is to perform once, how many ways can the program be arranged in each of the following cases?

(a) All girls must perform first.
(b) A girl must perform first and a boy must perform last.
(c) Elisa and Doug will perform first and last, respectively.
(d) The entire program will alternate between girls and boys.
(e) The first, eighth, and fifteenth performers must be girls.

41. *Scheduling Daily Reading* Carole begins each day by reading from one of seven inspirational books. How many ways can she choose the books for one week if the selection is done
(a) with replacement?
(b) without replacement?

42. *Counting Card Hands* How many of the possible 5-card hands from a standard 52-card deck would consist of the following cards?
(a) four clubs and one non-club
(b) two face cards and three non-face cards
(c) two red cards, two clubs, and a spade

43. *Dividing People into Groups* In how many ways could twenty-five people be divided into five groups containing, respectively, three, four, five, six, and seven people?

44. *Points and Lines in a Plane* If any two points determine a line, how many lines are determined by seven points in a plane, no three of which are collinear?

45. *Points and Triangles in a Plane* How many triangles are determined by twenty points in a plane, no three of which are collinear?

46. *Counting Possibilities on a Combination Lock* How many different three-number "combinations" are possible on a combination lock having 40 numbers on its dial? (*Hint:* "Combination" is a misleading name for these locks since repetitions are allowed and also order makes a difference.)

47. *Selecting Drivers and Passengers for a Trip* Michael Grant, his wife and son, and four additional friends are driving, in two vehicles, to the seashore.
(a) If all seven people can drive, how many ways can the two drivers be selected? (Everyone wants to drive the sports car, so it is important which driver gets which car.)
(b) If the sports car must be driven by Michael, his wife, or their son, how many ways can the drivers now be determined?
(c) If the sports car will accommodate only two people, and there are no other restrictions, how many ways can both drivers and passengers be assigned to both cars?

48. Winning the Daily Double in Horse Racing At the race track, you win the "daily double" by purchasing a ticket and selecting the winners of both of two specified races. If there are six and eight horses running in the first and second races, respectively, how many tickets must you purchase to guarantee a winning selection?

49. Winning the Trifecta in Horse Racing Many race tracks offer a "trifecta" race. You win by selecting the correct first-, second-, and third-place finishers. If eight horses are entered, how many tickets must you purchase to guarantee that one of them will be a trifecta winner?

50. Selecting Committee Members Nine people are to be distributed among three committees of two, three, and four members and a chairperson is to be selected for each committee. How many ways can this be done? (*Hint:* Break the task into the following sequence of parts.)
(a) Select the members of the two-person committee.
(b) Select the members of the three-person committee.
(c) Select the chair of the two-person committee.
(d) Select the chair of the three-person committee.
(e) Select the chair of the four-person committee.

51. Arranging New Home Models (See Exercise 29.) Because of his good work, Jeff Hubbard gets a contract to build homes on three additional blocks in the subdivision, with six homes on each block. He decides to build nine deluxe homes on these three blocks: two on the first block, three on the second, and four on the third. The remaining nine homes will be standard.
(a) Altogether on the three-block stretch, how many different choices does Jeff have for positioning the eighteen homes? (*Hint:* Consider the three blocks separately and use the fundamental counting principle.)
(b) How many choices would he have if he built 2, 3, and 4 deluxe models on the three different blocks as before, but not necessarily on the first, second, and third blocks in that order?

52. Building Numbers from Sets of Digits
(a) How many six-digit counting numbers use all six digits 4, 5, 6, 7, 8, and 9?
(b) Suppose all these numbers were arranged in increasing order: 456,789; 456,798; and so on. Which number would be 364th in the list?

53. Arranging a Wedding Reception Line At a wedding reception, the bride and groom, the maid of honor and best man, two bridesmaids, and two ushers will form a reception line. How many ways can they be arranged in each of the following cases?

(a) Any order will do.
(b) The bride and groom must be the last two in line.
(c) The groom must be last in line with the bride next to him.

54. Assigning Student Grades A professor teaches a class of 60 students and another class of 40 students. Five percent of the students in each class are to receive a grade of A. How many different ways can the A grades be distributed?

55. Sums of Digits How many counting numbers have four distinct nonzero digits such that the sum of the four digits is
(a) 12? (b) 13?

56. Screening Computer Processors A computer company will screen a shipment of 30 processors by testing a random sample of five of them. How many different samples are possible?

57. Verify that $_{12}C_9 = {}_{12}C_3$.

58. Use the factorial formula for combinations to prove that in general, $_nC_r = {}_nC_{n-r}$.

59. (a) Use the factorial formula for permutations to evaluate, for any whole number n, $_nP_0$.
(b) Explain the meaning of the result in part (a).

60. (a) Use the factorial formula for combinations and the definition of 0! to evaluate, for any whole number n, $_nC_0$.
(b) Explain the meaning of the result in part (a).

1.4 Using Pascal's Triangle

Pascal's Triangle • Applications

Start

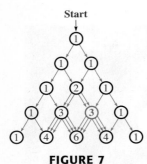

FIGURE 7

Pascal's Triangle

The triangular array in Figure 7 represents what we can call "random walks" that begin at START and proceed downward according to the following rule. At each circle (branch point), a coin is tossed. If it lands heads, we go downward to the left. If it lands tails, we go downward to the right. At each point, left and right are equally likely. In each circle we have recorded the number of different routes that could bring us to that point. For example, the colored 3 can be reached as the result of three different coin-tossing sequences: htt, tht, and tth.

Another way to generate the same pattern of numbers is to begin with 1s down both diagonals and then fill in the interior entries by adding the two numbers just above a given position (to the left and right). For example, the colored 28 in Table 5 is the result of adding 7 and 21 in the row above it.

TABLE 5 Pascal's Triangle

Row Number																					Row Sum
0										1											1
1									1		1										2
2								1		2		1									4
3							1		3		3		1								8
4						1		4		6		4		1							16
5					1		5		10		10		5		1						32
6				1		6		15		20		15		6		1					64
7			1		7		21		35		35		21		7		1				128
8		1		8		28		56		70		56		28		8		1			256
9	1		9		36		84		126		126		84		36		9		1		512
10	1	10		45		120		210		252		210		120		45		10	1		1024

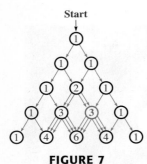

"Pascal's" triangle shown in the 1303 text ***Szu-yuen Yu-chien*** (*The Precious Mirror of the Four Elements*) by the Chinese mathematician Chu Shih-chieh.

By continuing to add pairs of numbers, we extend the array indefinitely downward, always beginning and ending each row with 1s. (The table shows just rows 0 through 10.) This unending "triangular" array of numbers is called **Pascal's triangle,** since Blaise Pascal wrote a treatise about it in 1653. There is evidence, though, that it was known as early as around 1100 and may have been studied in China or India still earlier.

At any rate, the "triangle" possesses many interesting properties. In counting applications, the most useful property is that, in general, entry number r in row number n is equal to $_nC_r$—the number of *combinations* of n things taken r at a time. This correspondence is shown (through row 7) in Table 6 on the next page.

TABLE 6 Combination Values in Pascal's Triangle

Row Number															
0								$_0C_0$							
1							$_1C_0$		$_1C_1$						
2						$_2C_0$		$_2C_1$		$_2C_2$					
3					$_3C_0$		$_3C_1$		$_3C_2$		$_3C_3$				
4				$_4C_0$		$_4C_1$		$_4C_2$		$_4C_3$		$_4C_4$			
5			$_5C_0$		$_5C_1$		$_5C_2$		$_5C_3$		$_5C_4$		$_5C_5$		
6		$_6C_0$		$_6C_1$		$_6C_2$		$_6C_3$		$_6C_4$		$_6C_5$		$_6C_6$	
7	$_7C_0$		$_7C_1$		$_7C_2$		$_7C_3$		$_7C_4$		$_7C_5$		$_7C_6$		$_7C_7$
							and so on								

Having a copy of Pascal's triangle handy gives us another option for evaluating combinations. Any time we need to know the number of combinations of n things taken r at a time (that is, the number of subsets of size r in a set of size n), we can simply read entry number r of row number n. Keep in mind that the *first row shown is row number 0*. Also, the first entry of each row can be called entry number 0. This entry gives the number of subsets of size 0 (which is always 1 since there is only one empty set).

Applications

EXAMPLE 1 Applying Pascal's Triangle to Counting People

A group of ten people includes six women and four men. If five of these people are randomly selected to fill out a questionnaire, how many different samples of five people are possible?

SOLUTION

Since this is simply a matter of selecting a subset of five from a set of ten (or combinations of ten things taken five at a time), we can read $_{10}C_5$ from row 10 of Pascal's triangle in Table 5. The answer is 252.

EXAMPLE 2 Applying Pascal's Triangle to Counting People

Among the 252 possible samples of five people in Example 1, how many of them would consist of exactly two women and three men?

SOLUTION

Two women can be selected from six women in $_6C_2$ different ways, and three men can be selected from four men in $_4C_3$ different ways. These combination values can be read from Pascal's triangle. Then, since the task of obtaining two women and three men requires both individual parts, the fundamental counting principle tells us to multiply the two values:

$$_6C_2 \cdot {_4C_3} = 15 \cdot 4 = 60.$$

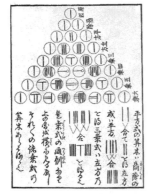

This **Japanese version** of the triangle dates from the eighteenth century. The "stick numerals" evolved from bamboo counting pieces used on a ruled board. Possibly Omar Khayyam, twelfth-century Persian mathematician and poet, may also have divined its patterns in pursuit of algebraic solutions. (The triangle lists the coefficients of the binomial expansion, explained in For Further Thought on page 39.)

> **EXAMPLE 3** **Applying Pascal's Triangle to Coin Tossing**

If five fair coins are tossed, in how many different ways could exactly three heads be obtained?

SOLUTION

There are various "ways" of obtaining exactly three heads because the three heads can occur on different subsets of the coins. For example, hhtht and thhth are just two of many possibilities. When such a possibility is written down, exactly three positions are occupied by an h, the other two by a t. Each distinct way of choosing three positions from a set of five positions gives a different possibility. (Once the three positions for h are determined, each of the other two positions automatically receives a t.) So our answer is just the number of size-three subsets of a size-five set, that is, the number of combinations of five things taken three at a time. We read this answer from row 5 of Pascal's triangle:

$$_5C_3 = 10.$$

Notice that row 5 of Pascal's triangle also provides answers to several other questions about tossing five fair coins. They are summarized in Table 7.

TABLE 7	Tossing Five Fair Coins	
Number of Heads n	**Ways of Obtaining Exactly n Heads**	**Listing**
0	$_5C_0 = 1$	ttttt
1	$_5C_1 = 5$	htttt, thttt, tthtt, tttht, tttth
2	$_5C_2 = 10$	hhttt, hthtt, httht, httth, thhtt, ththt, thtth, tthht, tthth, ttthh
3	$_5C_3 = 10$	hhhtt, hhtht, hhtth, hthht, hthth, htthh, thhht, thhth, ththh, tthhh
4	$_5C_4 = 5$	hhhht, hhhth, hhthh, hthhh, thhhh
5	$_5C_5 = 1$	hhhhh

To analyze the tossing of a different number of fair coins, we can simply take the pertinent numbers from a different row of Pascal's triangle. Repeated coin tossing is an example of a "binomial" experiment (because each toss has *two* possible outcomes, heads and tails). The likelihoods of various occurrences in such a situation will be addressed in Section 2.4 on binomial probability.

For Further Thought

The Binomial Theorem

The combination values, which comprise Pascal's triangle, also arise in a totally different mathematical context. In algebra, "binomial" refers to a two-term expression such as $x + y$, or $a + 2b$, or $w^3 - 4$. The first few powers of the binomial $x + y$ are shown here.

$$(x + y)^0 = 1$$
$$(x + y)^1 = x + y$$
$$(x + y)^2 = x^2 + 2xy + y^2$$
$$(x + y)^3 = x^3 + 3x^2y + 3xy^2 + y^3$$
$$(x + y)^4 = x^4 + 4x^3y + 6x^2y^2 + 4xy^3 + y^4$$
$$(x + y)^5 = x^5 + 5x^4y + 10x^3y^2 + 10x^2y^3$$
$$+ 5xy^4 + y^5$$

Notice that the numerical coefficients of these expansions form the first six rows of Pascal's triangle. In our study of counting, we have called these numbers *combinations*, but in the study of algebra, they are called *binomial coefficients* and are usually denoted $\binom{n}{r}$ rather than $_nC_r$.

Generalizing the pattern of the powers shown above yields the important result known as the **binomial theorem.**

Binomial Theorem

For any positive integer n,

$$(x + y)^n = \binom{n}{0} \cdot x^n + \binom{n}{1} \cdot x^{n-1}y$$

$$+ \binom{n}{2} \cdot x^{n-2}y^2 + \binom{n}{3} \cdot x^{n-3}y^3 +$$

$$\cdots + \binom{n}{n-1} \cdot xy^{n-1} + \binom{n}{n} \cdot y^n,$$

where each binomial coefficient can be calculated by the formula

$$\binom{n}{r} = \frac{n!}{r!(n-r)!}.$$

EXAMPLE   Applying the Binomial Theorem

Write out the binomial expansion for $(2a + 5)^4$.

SOLUTION

We take the initial coefficients from row 4 of Pascal's triangle and then simplify algebraically.

$$(2a + 5)^4$$
$$= \binom{4}{0} \cdot (2a)^4 + \binom{4}{1} \cdot (2a)^3 \cdot 5$$
$$+ \binom{4}{2} \cdot (2a)^2 \cdot 5^2 + \binom{4}{3} \cdot (2a) \cdot 5^3$$
$$+ \binom{4}{4} \cdot 5^4$$

Recall that $(xy)^n = x^n \cdot y^n$.

$$= 1 \cdot 2^4 \cdot a^4 + 4 \cdot 2^3 \cdot a^3 \cdot 5 + 6 \cdot 2^2 \cdot a^2 \cdot 5^2$$
$$+ 4 \cdot 2 \cdot a \cdot 5^3 + 1 \cdot 5^4$$
$$= 16\,a^4 + 160\,a^3 + 600\,a^2$$
$$+ 1000a + 625$$

For Group Discussion or Individual Investigation

Write out the binomial expansion for each of the following powers.

1. $(x + y)^6$
2. $(x + y)^7$
3. $(w + 4)^5$
4. $(4x + 2y)^4$
5. $(u - v)^6$
   (*Hint:* First change $u - v$ to $u + (-v)$.)
6. $(5m - 2n)^3$
7. How many terms are in the binomial expansion for $(x + y)^n$?
8. Identify the 15th term only of the expansion for $(a + b)^{18}$.

1.4 EXERCISES

Read each combination value directly from Pascal's triangle.

1. $_4C_2$ **2.** $_5C_3$ **3.** $_6C_3$

4. $_7C_5$ **5.** $_8C_5$ **6.** $_9C_6$

7. $_9C_2$ **8.** $_{10}C_7$

Selecting Committees of Congressmen *A committee of four Congressmen will be selected from a group of seven Democrats and three Republicans. Find the number of ways of obtaining each result.*

9. exactly one Democrat

10. exactly two Democrats

11. exactly three Democrats

12. exactly four Democrats

Tossing Coins *Suppose eight fair coins are tossed. Find the number of ways of obtaining each result.*

13. exactly three heads

14. exactly four heads

15. exactly five heads

16. exactly six heads

Selecting Classrooms *Peg Cheever, searching for an Economics class, knows that it must be in one of nine classrooms. Since the professor does not allow people to enter after the class has begun, and there is very little time left, Peg decides to try just four of the rooms at random.*

17. How many different selections of four rooms are possible?

18. How many of the selections of Exercise 17 will fail to locate the class?

19. How many of the selections of Exercise 17 will succeed in locating the class?

20. What fraction of the possible selections will lead to "success"? (Give three decimal places.)

For a set of five elements, find the number of different subsets of each size. (Use row 5 of Pascal's triangle to find the answers.)

21. 0 **22.** 1 **23.** 2

24. 3 **25.** 4 **26.** 5

27. How many subsets (of any size) are there for a set of five elements?

28. Find and explain the relationship between the row number and row sum in Pascal's triangle.

Over the years, many interesting patterns have been discovered in Pascal's triangle. * *We explore a few of them in Exercises 29–35.*

29. Refer to Table 5.
   (a) Choose a row whose row number is prime. Except for the 1s in this row, what is true of all the other entries?
   (b) Choose a second prime row number and see if the same pattern holds.
   (c) Use the usual method to construct row 11 in Table 5, and verify that the same pattern holds in that row.

30. Name the next five numbers of the diagonal sequence in the figure. What are these numbers called?

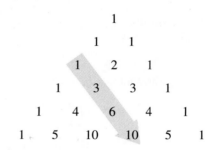

31. Complete the sequence of sums on the diagonals shown in the figure at the top of the next page. What pattern do these sums make? What is the name of this important sequence of numbers? The presence of this sequence in the triangle apparently was not recognized by Pascal.

*For example, see the article "Serendipitous Discovery of Pascal's Triangle" by Francis W. Stanley in *The Mathematics Teacher,* February 1975.

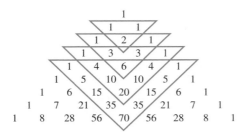

Sums
1
1
2
3
5

32. Construct another "triangle" by replacing every number in Pascal's triangle (rows **0** through **5**) by its remainder when divided by 2. What special property is shared by rows **2** and **4** of this new triangle?

33. What is the next row that would have the same property as rows **2** and **4** in Exercise 32?

34. How many even numbers are there in row **256** of Pascal's triangle? (Work Exercises 32 and 33 first.)

35. The figure shows a portion of Pascal's triangle with several inverted triangular regions outlined. For any one of these regions, what can be said of the sum of the squares of the entries across its top row?

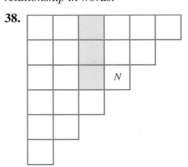

36. More than a century before Pascal's treatise on the "triangle" appeared, another work by the Italian mathematician Niccolo Tartaglia (1506–1559) came out and included the table of numbers shown here.

1	1	1	1	1	1
1	2	3	4	5	6
1	3	6	10	15	21
1	4	10	20	35	56
1	5	15	35	70	126
1	6	21	56	126	252
1	7	28	84	210	462
1	8	36	120	330	792

Explain the connection between Pascal's triangle and Tartaglia's "rectangle."

37. It was stated in the text that each interior entry in Pascal's triangle can be obtained by adding the two numbers just above it (to the left and right). This fact, known as the "Pascal identity," can be written as $_nC_r = {}_{n-1}C_{r-1} + {}_{n-1}C_r$. Use the factorial formula for combinations (along with some algebra) to prove the Pascal identity.

The "triangle" that Pascal studied and published in his treatise was actually more like a truncated corner of Tartaglia's rectangle, as shown here.

1	1	1	1	1	1	1	1	1	1
1	2	3	4	5	6	7	8	9	
1	3	6	10	15	21	28	36		
1	4	10	20	35	56	84			
1	5	15	35	70	126				
1	6	21	56	126					
1	7	28	84						
1	8	36							
1	9								
1									

Each number in the array can be calculated in various ways. In each of Exercises 38–41, consider the number N to be located anywhere in the array. By checking several locations in the given array, determine how N is related to the sum of all entries in the shaded cells. Describe the relationship in words.

38.

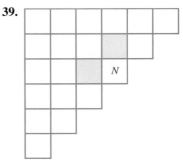

39.

40.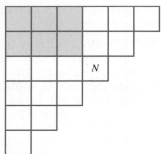

41.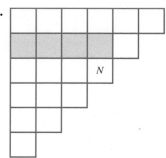

1.5 Counting Problems Involving "Not" and "Or"

Problems Involving "Not" • **Problems Involving "Or"**

The counting techniques in this section, which can be thought of as *indirect techniques*, are based on some useful correspondences between set theory, logic, and arithmetic, as shown in Table 8.

TABLE 8 Set Theory/Logic/Arithmetic Correspondences

	Set Theory	Logic	Arithmetic
Operation or Connective (Symbol)	Complement (′)	Not (∼)	Subtraction (−)
Operation or Connective (Symbol)	Union (∪)	Or (∨)	Addition (+)

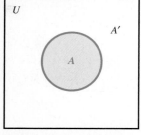

The complement of a set

FIGURE 8

Problems Involving "Not" Suppose U is the set of all possible results of some type. (All possibilities comprise the "universal set U," as discussed in Chapter 2.) Let A be the set of all those results that satisfy a given condition. For any set S, its cardinal number is written $n(S)$, and its complement is written S'. Figure 8 suggests that

$$n(A) + n(A') = n(U).$$

Also, $\quad n(A) = n(U) - n(A') \quad$ and $\quad n(A') = n(U) - n(A).$

We focus here on the form that expresses the following indirect counting principle (based on the complement/not/subtraction correspondence from Table 8).

> **Complements Principle of Counting**
>
> The number of ways a certain condition can be satisfied is the total number of possible results minus the number of ways the condition would **not** be satisfied. Symbolically, if A is any set within the universal set U, then
>
> $$n(A) = n(U) - n(A').$$

EXAMPLE 1   Counting the Proper Subsets of a Set

For the set $S = \{a, b, c, d, e, f\}$, find the number of proper subsets.

SOLUTION

Recall that a proper subset of S is any subset with fewer than all six elements. Subsets of several different sizes would satisfy this condition. However, it is easier to consider the one subset that is not proper, namely S itself. From set theory, we know that set S has a total of $2^6 = 64$ subsets. Thus, from the complements principle, the number of proper subsets is $64 - 1 = 63$. In words, the number of subsets that *are* proper is the total number of subsets minus the number of subsets that are *not* proper. ■

Consider the tossing of three fair coins. Since each coin will land either heads (h) or tails (t), the possible results can be listed as follows.

hhh, hht, hth, thh, htt, tht, tth, ttt   Results of tossing three fair coins

(Even without the listing, we could have concluded that there would be eight possibilities. There are two possible outcomes for each coin, so the fundamental counting principle gives $2 \cdot 2 \cdot 2 = 2^3 = 8$.)

Suppose we wanted the number of ways of obtaining *at least* one head. In this case, "at least one" means one or two or three. Rather than dealing with all three cases, we can note that "at least one" is the opposite (or complement) of "fewer than one" (which is zero). Because there is only one way to get zero heads (ttt), and there are a total of eight possibilities, the complements principle gives the number of ways of getting at least one head: $8 - 1 = 7$. (The number of outcomes that include at least one head is the total number of outcomes minus the number of outcomes that do *not* include at least one head.) We find that indirect counting methods can often be applied to problems involving "at least," or "at most," or "less than," or "more than."

EXAMPLE 2   Counting Coin-Tossing Results

If four fair coins are tossed, in how many ways can at least one tail be obtained?

SOLUTION

By the fundamental counting principle, $2^4 = 16$ different results are possible. Exactly one of these fails to satisfy the condition of "at least one tail" (namely, no tails, or hhhh). So our answer (from the complements principle) is $16 - 1 = 15$. ■

EXAMPLE 3   Counting Selections of Airliner Seats

Carol Britz and three friends are boarding an airliner just before departure time. There are only ten seats left, three of which are aisle seats. How many ways can the four people arrange themselves in available seats so that at least one of them sits on the aisle?

SOLUTION

The word "arrange" implies that order is important, so we shall use permutations. "At least one aisle seat" is the opposite (complement) of "no aisle seats." The total number of ways to arrange four people among ten seats is $_{10}P_4 = 5040$. The number of ways to arrange four people among seven (non-aisle) seats is $_7P_4 = 840$. Therefore, by the complements principle, the number of arrangements with at least one aisle seat is $5040 - 840 = 4200$. ■

Problems Involving "Or"   The complements principle is one way of counting indirectly. Another technique is to count the elements of a set by breaking that set into simpler component parts. If $S = A \cup B$, the cardinal number formula (from Section 2.4) says to find the number of elements in S by adding the number in A to the number in B. We must then subtract the number in the intersection $A \cap B$ if A and B are not disjoint, as in Figure 9. But if A and B are disjoint, as in Figure 10, the subtraction is not necessary.

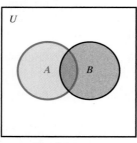

Nondisjoint sets

FIGURE 9

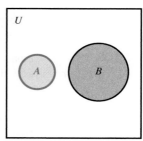

Disjoint sets

FIGURE 10

The following principle reflects the union/or/addition correspondence from Table 8.

Additive Principle of Counting

The number of ways that one **or** the other of two conditions could be satisfied is the number of ways one of them could be satisfied plus the number of ways the other could be satisfied minus the number of ways they could both be satisfied together.

If A and B are any two sets, then

$$n(A \cup B) = n(A) + n(B) - n(A \cap B).$$

If sets A and B are disjoint, then

$$n(A \cup B) = n(A) + n(B).$$

EXAMPLE 4   Counting Card Hands

How many five-card hands consist of either all clubs or all red cards?

SOLUTION

No hand that satisfies one of these conditions could also satisfy the other, so the two sets of possibilities (all clubs, all red cards) are disjoint. Therefore the second formula of the additive principle applies, and we obtain

$n(\text{all clubs } or \text{ all red cards}) = n(\text{all clubs}) + n(\text{all red cards})$ Additive counting principle

$= {}_{13}C_5 + {}_{26}C_5$ 13 clubs, 26 red cards

$= 1287 + 65{,}780$ Substitute values.

$= 67{,}067.$ ▪

```
(10 nPr 4)-(7 nP
r 4)
              4200
(13 nCr 5)+(26 n
Cr 5)
             67067
```

Results in Examples 3 and 4 are
supported in this screen.

EXAMPLE 5   Counting Selections from a Diplomatic Delegation

Table 9 categorizes a diplomatic delegation of 18 congressional members as to political party and gender. If one of the members is chosen randomly to be spokesperson for the group, in how many ways could that person be a Democrat or a woman?

TABLE 9

	Men (M)	Women (W)	Totals
Republican (R)	5	3	8
Democrat (D)	4	6	10
Totals	9	9	18

SOLUTION

Since D and W are not disjoint (6 delegates are both Democrats and women), the first formula of the additive principle is required.

$$\begin{aligned}
n(D \text{ or } W) &= n(D \cup W) && \text{Union/or correspondence} \\
&= n(D) + n(W) - n(D \cap W) && \text{Additive principle} \\
&= 10 + 9 - 6 && \text{Substitute values.} \\
&= 13.
\end{aligned}$$

EXAMPLE 6   Counting Course Selections for a Degree Program

Peggy Jenders needs to take twelve more specific courses for a bachelors degree, including four in math, three in physics, three in computer science, and two in business. If five courses are randomly chosen from these twelve for next semester's program, how many of the possible selections would include at least two math courses?

SOLUTION

Of all the information given here, what is important is that there are four math courses and eight other courses to choose from, and that five of them are being selected for next semester. If T denotes the set of selections that include at least two math courses, then we can write

$$T = A \cup B \cup C$$

where $A =$ the set of selections with exactly two math courses,
             $B =$ the set of selections with exactly three math courses,
and $C =$ the set of selections with exactly four math courses.

(In this case, *at least two* means exactly two **or** exactly three **or** exactly four.) The situation is illustrated in Figure 11. By previous methods, we know that

$$n(A) = {}_4C_2 \cdot {}_8C_3 = 6 \cdot 56 = 336,$$
$$n(B) = {}_4C_3 \cdot {}_8C_2 = 4 \cdot 28 = 112,$$
and $$n(C) = {}_4C_4 \cdot {}_8C_1 = 1 \cdot 8 = 8,$$

so that, by the additive principle,

$$n(T) = 336 + 112 + 8 = 456.$$

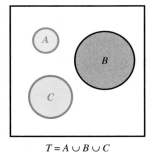

$T = A \cup B \cup C$

FIGURE 11

EXAMPLE 7   Counting Three-Digit Numbers with Conditions

How many three-digit counting numbers are multiples of 2 or multiples of 5?

SOLUTION

A multiple of 2 must end in an even digit (0, 2, 4, 6, or 8), so there are $9 \cdot 10 \cdot 5 = 450$ three-digit multiples of 2. A multiple of 5 must end in either 0 or 5, so there are $9 \cdot 10 \cdot 2 = 180$ of those. A multiple of both 2 and 5 is a multiple of 10 and must end in 0. There are $9 \cdot 10 \cdot 1 = 90$ of those. By the additive principle there are

$$450 + 180 - 90 = 540$$

possible three-digit numbers that are multiples of 2 or multiples of 5. ▨

EXAMPLE 8   Counting Card-Drawing Results

A single card is drawn from a standard 52-card deck.

(a) In how many ways could it be a heart or a king?
(b) In how many ways could it be a club or a face card?

SOLUTION

(a) A single card can be both a heart and a king (the king of hearts), so use the first additive formula. There are thirteen hearts, four kings, and one card that is both a heart and a king:
$$13 + 4 - 1 = 16.$$

(b) There are 13 clubs, 12 face cards, and 3 cards that are both clubs and face cards, giving
$$13 + 12 - 3 = 22.$$ ▨

EXAMPLE 9   Counting Subsets of a Set with Conditions

How many subsets of a 25-element set have more than three elements?

SOLUTION

It would be a real job to count directly all subsets of size 4, 5, 6, . . . , 25. It is much easier to count those with three or fewer elements and apply the complements principle.

There is	$_{25}C_0 = 1$	size-0 subset.
There are	$_{25}C_1 = 25$	size-1 subsets.
There are	$_{25}C_2 = 300$	size-2 subsets.
There are	$_{25}C_3 = 2300$	size-3 subsets.

The total number of subsets (of all sizes, 0 through 25) is $2^{25} = 33{,}554{,}432$ (use a calculator). So the number with more than three elements must be

$$33{,}554{,}432 - (1 + 25 + 300 + 2300) = 33{,}554{,}432 - 2626$$
$$= 33{,}551{,}806.$$ ▨

In Example 9, we used both the additive principle (to get the number of subsets with no more than three elements) and the complements principle.

> **PROBLEM-SOLVING HINT** As you work the exercises of this section, keep in mind that indirect methods may be best, and that you may also be able to use permutations, combinations, the fundamental counting principle, or listing procedures such as product tables or tree diagrams. Also, you may want to obtain combination values, when needed, from Pascal's triangle, or find combination and permutation values on a calculator.

1.5 EXERCISES

How many proper subsets are there of each set?

1. {A, B, C, D}

2. {u, v, w, x, y, z}

Tossing Coins *If you toss seven fair coins, in how many ways can you obtain each result?*

3. at least one head ("At least one" is the complement of "none.")

4. at least two heads ("At least two" is the complement of "zero or one.")

5. at least two tails

6. at least one of each (a head and a tail)

Rolling Dice *If you roll two fair dice (say red and green), in how many ways can you obtain each result? (Refer to Table 2 in Section 1.1.)*

7. at least 2 on the green die

8. a sum of at least 3

9. a 4 on at least one of the dice

10. a different number on each die

Drawing Cards *If you draw a single card from a standard 52-card deck, in how many ways can you obtain each result?*

11. a card other than the ace of spades

12. a nonface card

Identifying Properties of Counting Numbers *How many two-digit counting numbers meet each requirement?*

13. not a multiple of 10

14. greater than 70 or a multiple of 10

15. **Choosing Country Music Albums** Michelle Cook's collection of eight country music albums includes *When the Sun Goes Down* by Kenny Chesney. Michelle will choose three of her albums to play on a drive to Nashville. (Assume order is not important.)
   (a) How many different sets of three albums could she choose?
   (b) How many of these sets would not include *When the Sun Goes Down*?
   (c) How many of them would include *When the Sun Goes Down*?

16. **Choosing Broadway Hits** The ten longest Broadway runs include *The Phantom of the Opera* and *Les Misérables*. Four of the ten are chosen randomly. (Assume order is not important.)
   (a) How many ways can the four be chosen?
   (b) How many of those groups of four would include neither of the two productions mentioned?
   (c) How many of them would include at least one of the two productions mentioned?

17. **Choosing Days of the Week** How many different ways could three distinct days of the week be chosen so that at least one of them begins with the letter S? (Assume order of selection is not important.)

18. **Choosing School Assignments for Completion** Chalon Bridges has nine major assignments to complete for school this week. Two of them involve writing essays. Chalon decides to work on two of the nine assignments tonight. How many different choices of two would include at least one essay assignment? (Assume order is not important.)

Selecting Restaurants *Byron Hopkins wants to dine at three different restaurants during a visit to a mountain resort. If two of eight available restaurants serve seafood, find the* *number of ways that at least one of the selected restaurants will serve seafood given the following conditions.*

19. The order of selection is important.

20. The order of selection is not important.

21. *Seating Arrangements on an Airliner* Refer to Example 3. If one of the group decided at the last minute not to fly, then how many ways could the remaining three arrange themselves among the ten available seats so that at least one of them will sit on the aisle?

22. *Identifying Properties of Counting Numbers* Find the number of four-digit counting numbers containing at least one zero, under each of the following conditions.
(a) Repeated digits are allowed.
(b) Repeated digits are not allowed.

23. *Selecting Faculty Committees* A committee of four faculty members will be selected from a department of twenty-five which includes professors Fontana and Spradley. In how many ways could the committee include at least one of these two professors?

24. *Selecting Search and Rescue Teams* A Civil Air Patrol unit of twelve members includes four officers. In how many ways can four members be selected for a search and rescue mission such that at least one officer is included?

Drawing Cards If a single card is drawn from a standard 52-card deck, in how many ways could it be the following? (Use the additive principle.)

25. a club or a jack

26. a face card or a black card

Counting Students Who Enjoy Music and Literature Of a group of 50 students, 30 enjoy music, 15 enjoy literature, and 10 enjoy both music and literature. How many of them enjoy the following?

27. at least one of these two subjects (Use the additive principle.)

28. neither of these two subjects (complement of "at least one")

Counting Hands of Cards Among the 2,598,960 possible 5-card poker hands from a standard 52-card deck, how many contain the following cards?

29. at least one card that is not a club (complement of "all clubs")

30. cards of more than one suit (complement of "all the same suit")

31. at least one face card (complement of "no face cards")

32. at least one diamond, but not all diamonds (complement of "no diamonds or all diamonds")

The Size of Subsets of a Set If a given set has twelve elements, how many of its subsets have the given numbers of elements?

33. at most two elements

34. at least ten elements

35. more than two elements

36. from three through nine elements

37. *Counting License Numbers* If license numbers consist of three letters followed by three digits, how many different licenses could be created having at least one letter or digit repeated? (*Hint:* Use the complements principle of counting.)

38. *Drawing Cards* If two cards are drawn from a 52-card deck without replacement (that is, the first card is not replaced in the deck before the second card is drawn), in how many different ways is it possible to obtain a king on the first draw and a heart on the second? (*Hint:* Split this event into the two disjoint components "king of hearts and then another heart" and "non-heart king and then heart." Use the fundamental counting principle on each component, then apply the additive principle.)

39. Extend the additive counting principle to three overlapping sets (as in the figure) to show that

$$n(A \cup B \cup C) = n(A) + n(B) + n(C)$$
$$- n(A \cap B) - n(A \cap C)$$
$$- n(B \cap C) + n(A \cap B \cap C).$$

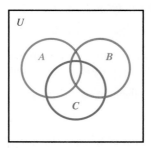

40. How many of the counting numbers 1 through 300 are *not* divisible by 2, 3, or 5? (*Hint:* Use the complements principle and the result of Exercise 39.)

Selecting National Monuments to Visit *Edward Roberts is planning a long-awaited driving tour, which will take him and his family on the southern route to the West Coast. Ed is interested in seeing the twelve national monuments listed here, but will have to settle for seeing just three of them because some family members are anxious to get to Disneyland.*

New Mexico	Arizona	California
Gila Cliff Dwellings	Canyon de Chelly	Devils Postpile
Petroglyph	Organ Pipe Cactus	Joshua Tree
White Sands	Saguaro	Lava Beds
Aztec Ruins		Muir Woods
		Pinnacles

In how many ways could the three monuments chosen include the following?

41. sites in only one state

42. at least one site not in California

43. sites in fewer than all three states

44. sites in exactly two of the three states

Counting Categories of Poker Hands *Table 4 in this chapter (For Further Thought in Section 1.3) described the various kinds of hands in 5-card poker. Verify each statement in Exercises 45–48. (Explain all steps of your argument.)*

45. There are four ways to get a royal flush.

46. There are 36 ways to get a straight flush.

47. There are 10,200 ways to get a straight.

48. There are 54,912 ways to get three of a kind.

49. Explain why the complements principle of counting is called an "indirect" method.

50. Explain the difference between the two formulas of the additive principle of counting.

COLLABORATIVE INVESTIGATION

Solving a Traveling Salesman Problem

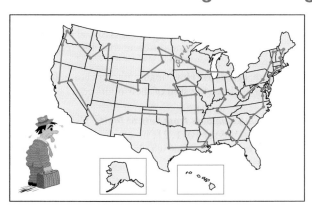

In 1985, Shen Lin came up with the route shown above for a salesman wanting to visit all capital cities in the forty-eight contiguous states, starting and ending at the same capital and traveling the shortest possible total distance. He could not prove that his 10,628-mile route was the shortest possible, but he offered $100 to anyone who could find a shorter one.

This is an example of a classic problem, the so-called **traveling salesman problem** (or **TSP**), which has many practical applications in business and industry but has baffled mathematicians for years. In the case above, there are 47! possible routes, although many of them can be quickly eliminated, leaving $\frac{24!}{3}$ possibilities to consider. This is still a 24-digit number, far too large for even state-of-the-art computers to analyze directly.

Although computer scientists have so far failed to find an "efficient algorithm" to solve the general traveling salesman problem, successes are periodically achieved for particular cases. In 1998, Rice University researchers David Applegate, Robert Bixby, and William Cook, along with Vasek Chvatal of Rutgers University, announced a breakthrough solution to the traveling salesman problem for 13,509 U.S. cities with populations of at least 500 people. In 2004, the solution was found for a case with 24,978 points to visit.

A much smaller set (of seven cities, A through G), which can be completely analyzed using a calculator, is shown here.

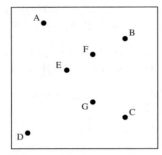

Notice that certain routes clearly are *not* the shortest. For example, it is apparent that the route ACEDFGBA involves too much jumping back and forth across the diagram to result in the least possible total distance. (In fact, the total distance for this route is 360 miles, considerably more than necessary.) The fifteen distances given

here (in miles) between pairs of cities should be sufficient data for computing the shortest possible route.

AB = 51   AF = 36   BF = 22   CG = 22   EF = 22

AD = 71   BC = 50   BG = 45   DE = 45   EG = 28

AE = 32   BE = 45   CD = 61   DG = 45   FG = 30

Topics for Discussion

Divide the class into groups of 3 or 4 students each. Each group is to do the following.

1. Study the drawing, and make a list of all routes that you think may be the shortest.
2. For each candidate route, add the appropriate seven terms to get a total distance.
3. Arrive at a group consensus as to which route is shortest.

Now bring the whole class back together, and do the following.

1. Make a list of routes, with total distances, that the various groups thought were shortest.
2. Observe whether the different groups all agreed on which route was shortest.
3. As a class, try to achieve a consensus on the shortest route. Do you think that someone else may be able to find a shorter one?

CHAPTER 1 TEST

If digits may be used from the set {0, 1, 2, 3, 4, 5, 6}, find the number of possibilities in each category.

1. three-digit numbers

2. even three-digit numbers

3. three-digit numbers without repeated digits

4. three-digit multiples of five without repeated digits

5. ***Counting Triangles in a Figure*** Determine the number of triangles (of any size) in the figure shown here.

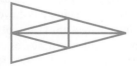

6. ***Tossing Coins*** Construct a tree diagram showing all possible results when a fair coin is tossed four times, if the third toss must be different than the second.

7. ***Sums of Digits*** How many nonrepeating four-digit numbers have the sum of their digits equal to 30?

8. ***Building Numbers from Sets of Digits*** Using only digits from the set {0, 1, 2}, how many three-digit numbers can be written which have no repeated odd digits?

Evaluate each expression.

9. 5!

10. $\dfrac{8!}{5!}$

11. $_{12}P_4$

12. $_7C_3$

13. ***Building Words from Sets of Letters*** How many five-letter "words" without repeated letters are possible using the English alphabet? (Assume that any five letters make a "word.")

14. ***Building Words from Sets of Letters*** Using the Russian alphabet (which has 32 letters), and allowing repeated letters, how many five-letter "words" are possible?

Scheduling Assignments *Andrea has seven homework assignments to complete. She wants to do four of them on Tuesday and the other three on Wednesday.*

15. In how many ways can she order Tuesday's work?

16. Assuming she finishes Tuesday's work successfully, in how many ways can she order Wednesday's work?

Arranging Letters *Find the number of distinguishable arrangements of the letters of each word.*

17. TATTLE   18. OLIGOPOLY

Selecting Groups of Basketball Players *If there are twelve players on a basketball team, find the number of choices the coach has in selecting each of the following.*

19. four players to carry the team equipment

20. two players for guard positions and two for forward positions

21. five starters and five subs

22. a set of three or more of the players

Choosing Switch Settings *Determine the number of possible settings for a row of four on–off switches under each condition.*

23. There are no restrictions.

24. The first and fourth switches must be on.

25. The first and fourth switches must be set the same.

26. No two adjacent switches can both be off.

27. No two adjacent switches can be set the same.

28. At least two switches must be on.

Choosing Subsets of Letters *Four distinct letters are to be chosen from the set*

$$\{A, B, C, D, E, F, G\}.$$

Determine the number of ways to obtain a subset that includes each of the following.

29. the letter D

30. both A and E

31. either A or E, but not both

32. equal numbers of vowels and consonants

33. more consonants than vowels

34. State the fundamental counting principle in your own words.

35. If $_nC_r = 495$ and $_nC_{r+1} = 220$, find the value of $_{n+1}C_{r+1}$.

36. If you write down the second entry of each row of Pascal's triangle (starting with row 1), what sequence of numbers do you obtain?

37. Explain why there are $r!$ permutations of n things taken r at a time corresponding to each combination of n things taken r at a time.

2

PROBABILITY

Suppose you're on a game show, and you're given the choice of three doors: Behind one of the doors is a car, and behind the other doors, goats. Of course, you want to win the car. You pick one of the doors, say Door 1, and the host, who knows what's behind the other doors, opens another door, say Door 3, to reveal a goat. He then says to you, "Do you want to change your choice?" Is it to your advantage to switch to Door 2?

This question appeared in *Parade* magazine in a column written by Marilyn vos Savant in the early 1990s. This probability problem, known as the Monty Hall Problem, was named after the host of the popular game show *Let's Make a Deal*. Marilyn's answer caused an incredible amount of discussion and argument among the general public at that time. The problem and an explanation of its answer were presented by Charlie Eppes in his "Math for Non-Mathematicians" class in the May 13, 2005, episode "Man Hunt" of the CBS series *NUMB3RS*.

The answers and its justification can also be found at the interactive Web site www.math.ucsd.edu/~crypto/Monty/monty.html. *Would YOU switch doors*? (See page 93 for the answer.)

2.1 Basic Concepts

**Historical Background • Probability • The Law of Large Numbers
• Probability in Genetics • Odds**

Christiaan Huygens
(1629–1695), a brilliant Dutch
mathematician and scientist, was
the first to write a formal treatise
on **probability.** It appeared in
1657 and was based on the
Pascal–Fermat correspondence.

Historical Background   Nearly all of the limited work in probability from the fifteenth through the eighteenth century concerned games and gambling. For example, in 1654, two French mathematicians, Pierre de Fermat (about 1601–1665) and Blaise Pascal (1623–1662), corresponded with each other regarding a problem posed by the Chevalier de Méré, a gambler and member of the aristocracy. *If the two players of a game are forced to quit before the game is finished, how should the pot be divided?* Pascal and Fermat solved the problem by developing basic methods of determining each player's chance, or probability, of winning.

One of the first to apply probability to matters other than gambling was the French mathematician Pierre Simon de Laplace (1749–1827), who is usually credited with being the "father" of probability theory.

But it was not until the twentieth century that a coherent mathematical theory of probability had been developed. It came mainly through a line of remarkable scholars in Russia, including P. L. Chebyshev (1821–1922), his student A. A. Markov (1856–1922), and finally Andrei Nikolaevich Kolmogorov (1903–1987), whose *Foundations of the Theory of Probability* was published in 1933.

Probability   If you go to a supermarket and select five pounds of peaches at 89¢ per pound, you can easily predict the amount you will be charged at the checkout counter: $5 \cdot \$.89 = \$4.45$. The amount charged for such purchases is a **deterministic phenomenon.** It can be predicted exactly on the basis of obtainable information, namely, in this case, number of pounds and cost per pound.

On the other hand, consider the problem faced by the produce manager of the market, who must order peaches to have on hand each day without knowing exactly how many pounds customers will buy during the day. The customer demand is an example of a **random phenomenon.** It fluctuates in such a way that its value (on a given day) cannot be predicted exactly with obtainable information.

The study of probability is concerned with such random phenomena. Even though we cannot be certain whether a given result will occur, we often can obtain a good measure of its *likelihood,* or **probability.** This chapter discusses various ways of finding and using probabilities.

In the study of probability, we say that any observation, or measurement, of a random phenomenon is an **experiment.** The possible results of the experiment are called **outcomes,** and the set of all possible outcomes is called the **sample space.**

Usually we are interested in some particular collection of the possible outcomes. Any such subset of the sample space is called an **event.** Outcomes that belong to the event are commonly referred to as "favorable outcomes," or "successes." Any time a success is observed, we say that the event has "occurred." The probability of an event, being a numerical measure of the event's likelihood, is determined in one of two ways, either *empirically* (experimentally) or *theoretically* (mathematically).

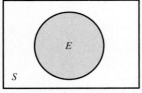

Every event is a subset of the sample space.

EXAMPLE 1 Finding Probability When Tossing a Coin

If a single coin is tossed, find the probability that it will land heads up.

SOLUTION

There is no apparent reason for one side of a coin to land up any more often than the other (in the long run), so we would normally assume that heads and tails are equally likely. We express this assumption by saying that the coin is "fair."

Now the experiment here is the tossing of a single fair coin, the sample space is $S = \{h, t\}$, and the event whose probability we seek is $E = \{h\}$. Since one of two possible outcomes is a head, the probability of heads is the quotient of 1 and 2.

$$\text{Probability (heads)} = \frac{1}{2}, \quad \text{written} \quad P(\text{h}) = \frac{1}{2} \quad \text{or} \quad P(E) = \frac{1}{2}.$$

EXAMPLE 2 Finding Probability When Tossing a Cup

If a Styrofoam cup is tossed, find the probability that it will land on its top.

SOLUTION

Intuitively, it seems that a cup will land on its side much more often than on its top or its bottom. But just how much more often is not clear. To get an idea, we performed the experiment of tossing such a cup 50 times. It landed on its side 44 times, on its top 5 times, and on its bottom just 1 time. By the frequency of "success" in this experiment, we concluded that

$$P(\text{top}) \approx \frac{5}{50} = \frac{1}{10}. \quad \longleftarrow \quad \textit{Write in lowest terms.}$$

In Example 1 involving the tossing of a fair coin, the number of possible outcomes was obviously two, both were equally likely, and one of the outcomes was a head. No actual experiment was required. The desired probability was obtained *theoretically*. Theoretical probabilities apply to all kinds of games of chance (dice rolling, card games, roulette, lotteries, and so on), and also apparently to many phenomena in nature.

Laplace, in his famous *Analytic Theory of Probability,* published in 1812, gave a formula that applies to any such theoretical probability, as long as the sample space S is finite and all outcomes are equally likely. (It is sometimes referred to as the *classical definition of probability.*)

Theoretical Probability Formula

If all outcomes in a sample space S are equally likely, and E is an event within that sample space, then the **theoretical probability** of event E is given by

$$P(E) = \frac{\text{number of favorable outcomes}}{\text{total number of outcomes}} = \frac{n(E)}{n(S)}.$$

On the other hand, Example 2 involved the tossing of a cup, where the likelihoods of the various outcomes were not intuitively clear. It took an actual experiment to arrive at a probability value of $\frac{1}{10}$, and that value, based on a portion of all possible tosses of the cup, should be regarded as an approximation of the true theoretical probability. The value was found according to the *experimental,* or *empirical,* probability formula.

> ### Empirical Probability Formula
>
> If E is an event that may happen when an experiment is performed, then the **empirical probability** of event E is given by
>
> $$P(E) \approx \frac{\text{number of times event } E \text{ occurred}}{\text{number of times the experiment was performed}}.$$

In 1827, **Robert Brown** (1773–1858), a Scottish physician and botanist, described the irregular motion of microscopic pollen grains suspended in water. Such "Brownian motion," as it came to be called, was not understood until 1905 when Albert Einstein explained it by treating molecular motion as a random phenomenon.

Usually it is clear in applications which of the two probability formulas should be used.

EXAMPLE 3   Finding the Probability of Having Daughters

Michelle Brown wants to have exactly two daughters. Assuming that boy and girl babies are equally likely, find her probability of success if

(a) she has a total of two children,

(b) she has a total of three children.

SOLUTION

(a) The equal likelihood assumption here allows the use of theoretical probability. But how can we determine the number of favorable outcomes and the total number of possible outcomes?

One way is to use a tree diagram (Section 1.1) to enumerate the possibilities, as shown in Figure 1. From the outcome column we obtain the sample space $S = \{gg, gb, bg, bb\}$. Only one outcome, marked with an arrow, is favorable to the event of exactly two daughters: $E = \{gg\}$. By the theoretical probability formula,

$$P(E) = \frac{n(E)}{n(S)} = \frac{1}{4}.$$

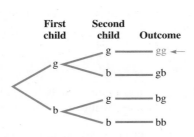

Exactly two girls among two children

FIGURE 1

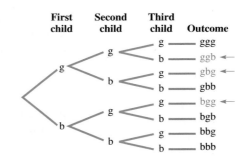

Exactly two girls among three children

FIGURE 2

(b) For three children altogether, we construct another tree diagram, as shown in Figure 2. In this case, we see that $S = \{ggg, ggb, gbg, gbb, bgg, bgb, bbg, bbb\}$ and $E = \{ggb, gbg, bgg\}$, so $P(E) = \frac{3}{8}$.

TABLE 1

Number of Poker Hands in 5-Card Poker; Nothing Wild

Event E	Number of Outcomes Favorable to E
Royal flush	4
Straight flush	36
Four of a kind	624
Full house	3744
Flush	5108
Straight	10,200
Three of a kind	54,912
Two pairs	123,552
One pair	1,098,240
No pair	1,302,540
Total	**2,598,960**

■ **EXAMPLE 4 Finding Probability When Dealing Cards**

Find the probability of being dealt each of the following hands in five-card poker. Use a calculator to obtain answers to eight decimal places.

(a) a full house (three of one denomination and two of another)
(b) a royal flush (the five highest cards—ace, king, queen, jack, ten—of a single suit)

SOLUTION

(a) Table 1 summarizes the various possible kinds of five-card hands. Since the 2,598,960 possible individual hands all are equally likely, we can enter the appropriate numbers from the table into the theoretical probability formula.

$$P(\text{full house}) = \frac{3744}{2,598,960} = \frac{6}{4165} \approx .00144058$$

(b) The table shows that there are four royal flushes, one for each suit, so that

$$P(\text{royal flush}) = \frac{4}{2,598,960} = \frac{1}{649,740} \approx .00000154. \qquad ■$$

Examples 3 and 4 both utilized the theoretical probability formula because we were able to enumerate all possible outcomes and all were equally likely. In Example 3, however, the equal likelihood of girl and boy babies was *assumed*. In fact, male births typically occur a little more frequently. (At the same time, there usually are more females living at any given time, due to higher infant mortality rates among males and longer female life expectancy in general.) Example 5 shows a way of incorporating such empirical information.

■ **EXAMPLE 5 Finding the Probability of the Gender of a Resident**

In the year 2003, the U.S. populace included 143,037,000 males and 147,773,000 females. If a person was selected randomly from the population in that year, what is the probability that the person would be a female?

SOLUTION

In this case, we calculate the empirical probability from the given experimental data.

$$P(\text{female}) = \frac{\text{number of female residents}}{\text{total number of residents}}$$

$$= \frac{147,773,000}{143,037,000 + 147,773,000}$$

$$\approx .508 \qquad ■$$

The Law of Large Numbers Now think again about the cup of Example 2. If we tossed it 50 more times, we would have 100 total tosses upon which to base an empirical probability of the cup landing on its top. The new value would likely be (at least slightly) different from what we obtained before. It would still be an empirical probability, but it would be "better" in the sense that it is based upon a larger set of outcomes.

The **law of large numbers** also can be stated as follows.

A theoretical probability really says nothing about one, or even a few, repetitions of an experiment, but only about the proportion of successes we would expect over the long run.

As we increase the number of tosses, the resulting empirical probability values may approach some particular number. If so, that number can be defined as the theoretical probability of that particular cup landing on its top. This "limiting" value can occur only as the actual number of observed tosses approaches the total number of possible tosses of the cup. Since there are potentially an infinite number of possible tosses, we could never actually find the theoretical probability we want. But we can still assume such a number exists. And as the number of actual observed tosses increases, the resulting empirical probabilities should tend ever closer to the theoretical value. This very important principle is known as the **law of large numbers** (or sometimes as the "law of averages").

Law of Large Numbers

As an experiment is repeated more and more times, the proportion of outcomes favorable to any particular event will tend to come closer and closer to the theoretical probability of that event.

EXAMPLE 6   Graphing a Sequence of Proportions

A fair coin was tossed 35 times, producing the following sequence of outcomes.

tthhh   ttthh   hthtt   hhthh   ttthh   thttt   hhthh

Calculate the ratio of heads to total tosses after the first toss, the second toss, and so on through all 35 tosses, and plot these ratios on a graph.

SOLUTION

After the first toss, we have 0 heads out of 1 toss, for a ratio of $\frac{0}{1}$ = .00. After two tosses, we have $\frac{0}{2}$ = .00. After three tosses, we have $\frac{1}{3}$ = .33. Verify that the first six ratios are

$$.00, \ .00, \ .33, \ .50, \ .60, \ .50.$$

The thirty-five ratios are plotted as points in Figure 3. Notice that the fluctuations away from .50 become smaller as the number of tosses increases, and the ratios appear to approach .50 toward the right side of the graph, in keeping with the law of large numbers.

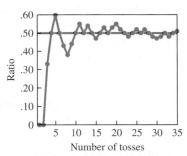

Ratio of heads to total tosses

FIGURE 3

Gregor Johann Mendel
(1822–1884) came from a peasant
family who managed to send him
to school. By 1847 he had been
ordained and was teaching at the
Abbey of St. Thomas. He finished
his education at the University of
Vienna and returned to the abbey
to teach mathematics and natural
science. Mendel began to carry out
experiments on plants in the abbey
garden, notably pea plants, whose
distinct traits (unit characters) he
had puzzled over. In 1865 he
published his results. (The Czech
stamp above commemorates the
centennial.) His work was not
appreciated at the time even
though he had laid the foundation
of **classical genetics.** Mendel
had established the basic laws of
heredity: laws of unit characters,
of dominance, and of segregation.

The law of large numbers provides an important connection between empirical and theoretical probabilities. Having obtained, by experiment, an empirical probability for an event, we can then, by inductive reasoning, *estimate* that event's theoretical probability. The more repetitions the estimate is based upon, the more reliable it is.

Likewise, if we know the theoretical probability of an event, we can then, by deductive reasoning, *predict* (estimate) the fraction of times the event will occur in a series of repeated experiments. The prediction should be more accurate for larger numbers of repetitions.

Probability in Genetics
Probabilities, both empirical and theoretical, have been valuable tools in many areas of science. An important early example was the work of the Austrian monk Gregor Mendel, who used the idea of randomness to help establish the study of genetics. Mendel published his results in 1865, but they were largely ignored until 1900 when others rediscovered and recognized the importance of his work.

In an effort to understand the mechanism of character transmittal from one generation to the next in plants, Mendel counted the number of occurrences of various characteristics. For example, he found that the flower color in certain pea plants obeyed this scheme:

Pure red crossed with pure white produces red.

Mendel theorized that red is "dominant" (symbolized with the capital letter R), while white is "recessive" (symbolized with the lowercase letter r). The pure red parent carried only genes for red (R), and the pure white parent carried only genes for white (r). The offspring would receive one gene from each parent, hence one of the four combinations shown in the body of Table 2. Because every offspring receives one gene for red, that characteristic dominates and the offspring exhibits the color red.

TABLE 2 First to Second Generation

| | | Second Parent | |
		r	r
First	**R**	Rr	Rr
Parent	**R**	Rr	Rr

Now each of these second-generation offspring, though exhibiting the color red, still carries one of each gene. So when two of them are crossed, each third-generation offspring will receive one of the gene combinations shown in Table 3. Mendel theorized that each of these four possibilities would be equally likely, and produced experimental counts that were close enough to support this hypothesis. (In more recent years, some have accused Mendel, or his assistants, of fudging the experimental data, but his conclusions have not been disputed.)

TABLE 3 Second to Third Generation

| | | Second Parent | |
		R	r
First	**R**	RR	Rr
Parent	**r**	rR	rr

Smoking 1.4 cigarettes
Spending 1 hour in a coal mine
Living 2 days in New York or Boston
Eating 40 teaspoons of peanut butter
Living 2 months with a cigarette smoker
Flying 1000 miles in a jet
Traveling 300 miles in a car
Riding 10 miles on a bicycle

Risk is the probability that a harmful event will occur. Almost every action or substance exposes a person to some risk, and the assessment and reduction of risk accounts for a great deal of study and effort in our world. The list above, from *Calculated Risk*, by J. Rodricks, contains activities that carry an annual increased risk of death by one chance in a million.

EXAMPLE 7   Finding Probabilities of Flower Colors

Referring to Table 3 on the previous page, determine the probability that a third-generation offspring will exhibit each of the following flower colors. Base the probabilities on the following sample space of equally likely outcomes: $S = \{RR, Rr, rR, rr\}$.

(a) red   **(b)** white

SOLUTION

(a) Since red dominates white, any combination with at least one gene for red (R) will result in red flowers. Since three of the four possibilities meet this criterion, $P(\text{red}) = \frac{3}{4}$.

(b) Only the combination rr has no gene for red, so $P(\text{white}) = \frac{1}{4}$.

Due to the probabilistic laws of genetics, vast improvements have resulted in food supply technology, through hybrid animal and crop development. Also, the understanding and control of human diseases have been advanced by related studies.

Odds   Whereas probability compares the number of favourable outcomes to the total number of outcomes, **odds** compare the number of favorable outcomes to the number of unfavorable outcomes. Odds are commonly quoted, rather than probabilities, in horse racing, lotteries, and most other gambling situations. And the odds quoted normally are odds "against" rather than odds "in favor."

Odds

If all outcomes in a sample space are equally likely, a of them are favorable to the event E, and the remaining b outcomes are unfavorable to E, then the **odds in favor** of E are a to b, and the **odds against** E are b to a.

EXAMPLE 8   Finding the Odds of Getting a Resort Job

Jennifer has been promised one of six summer jobs, three of which would be at a nearby beach resort. If she has equal chances for all six jobs, find the odds that she will land one at the resort.

SOLUTION

Since three possibilities are favorable and three are not, the odds of working at the resort are 3 to 3, or 1 to 1. (The common factor of 3 has been divided out.) Odds of 1 to 1 are often termed "even odds," or a "50–50 chance."

EXAMPLE 9   Finding the Odds of Winning a Raffle

Donn Demaree has purchased six tickets for an office raffle where the winner will receive an iPod unit. If 51 tickets were sold altogether and each has an equal chance of winning, what are the odds against Donn's winning the iPod?

SOLUTION

Donn has six chances to win and 45 chances to lose, so the odds against winning are 45 to 6, or 15 to 2. We simplify an odds ratio, just as a fraction.

▮ **EXAMPLE 10   Converting from Probability to Odds**

Suppose the probability of rain tomorrow is .13. Give this information in terms of odds.

SOLUTION

We can say that

$$P(\text{rain}) = .13 = \frac{13}{100}. \longleftarrow \begin{array}{l}\textit{Convert the decimal}\\ \textit{fraction to a quotient}\\ \textit{of integers.}\end{array}$$

This fraction does not mean there are necessarily 13 favorable outcomes and 100 possible outcomes, only that they would occur in this *ratio*. The corresponding number of *unfavorable* outcomes would be

$$100 - 13 = 87. \quad \text{(Total } - \text{favorable} = \text{unfavorable)}$$

So the odds are 13 to 87 in favor; we can say the odds are 87 to 13 against rain tomorrow. ▮

▮ **EXAMPLE 11   Converting from Odds to Probability**

In a certain sweepstakes, your odds of winning are 1 to 99,999,999. What is the probability you will win?

SOLUTION

The given odds provide a ratio of 1 favorable and 99,999,999 unfavorable outcomes, therefore $1 + 99{,}999{,}999 = 100{,}000{,}000$ total outcomes. So

$$P(\text{win}) = \frac{\text{favorable}}{\text{total}} = \frac{1}{100{,}000{,}000} = .00000001. \qquad ▮$$

2.1 EXERCISES

*In each of Exercises 1–4, give the probability that the spinner shown would land on **(a)** red, **(b)** yellow, **(c)** blue.*

1. 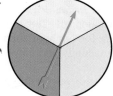   **2.** 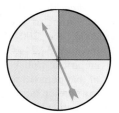   **3.** 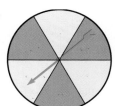   **4.**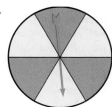

Solve each probability problem.

5. Using Spinners to Generate Numbers Suppose the spinner shown here is spun once, to determine a single-digit number, and we are interested in the event *E* that the resulting number is odd. Give each of the following.
(a) the sample space
(b) the number of favorable outcomes
(c) the number of unfavorable outcomes
(d) the total number of possible outcomes
(e) the probability of an odd number
(f) the odds in favor of an odd number

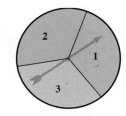

6. Lining Up Preschool Children Lynn Damme's group of preschool children includes eight girls and five boys. If Lynn randomly selects one child to be first in line, with *E* being the event that the one selected is a girl, give each of the following.
(a) the total number of possible outcomes
(b) the number of favorable outcomes
(c) the number of unfavorable outcomes
(d) the probability of event *E*
(e) the odds in favor of event *E*

7. Using Spinners to Generate Numbers The spinner of Exercise 5 is spun twice in succession to determine a two-digit number. Give each of the following.
(a) the sample space
(b) the probability of an odd number
(c) the probability of a number with repeated digits
(d) the probability of a number greater than 30
(e) the probability of a prime number

8. Probabilities in Coin Tossing Two fair coins are tossed (say a dime and a quarter). Give each of the following.
(a) the sample space
(b) the probability of heads on the dime
(c) the probability of heads on the quarter
(d) the probability of getting both heads
(e) the probability of getting the same outcome on both coins

9. Drawing Balls from an Urn Anne Kelly randomly chooses a single ball from the urn shown here. Find the odds in favor of each event.
(a) red
(b) yellow
(c) blue

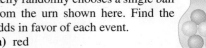

10. Random Selection of Club Officers Five people (Alan, Bill, Cathy, David, and Evelyn) form a club *N* = {A, B, C, D, E}. If they choose a president randomly, find the odds against each result.
(a) Cathy   (b) a woman
(c) a person whose name begins with a consonant

11. Random Selection of Fifties Music "Jukebox" Joe has fifty hit singles from the fifties, including exactly one by Buddy Holly, two by The Drifters, three by Bobby Darin, four by The Coasters, and five by Fats Domino. If Joe randomly selects one hit from his collection of fifty, find the probability it will be by each of the following.
(a) Buddy Holly   (b) The Drifters
(c) Bobby Darin   (d) The Coasters
(e) Fats Domino

12. Probabilities in Coin Tossing Three fair coins are tossed.
(a) Write out the sample space.

Determine the probability of each event.
(b) no heads   (c) exactly one head
(d) exactly two heads   (e) three heads

13. Number Sums for Rolling Two Dice The sample space for the rolling of two fair dice appeared in Table 2 of Section 1.1. Reproduce that table, but replace each of the 36 equally likely ordered pairs with its corresponding sum (for the two dice). Then find the probability of rolling each sum.
(a) 2   (b) 3   (c) 4
(d) 5   (e) 6   (f) 7
(g) 8   (h) 9   (i) 10
(j) 11   (k) 12

In Exercises 14 and 15, compute answers to three decimal places.

14. Probability of Seed Germination In a hybrid corn research project, 200 seeds were planted, and 170 of them germinated. Find the empirical probability that any particular seed of this type will germinate.

15. Probabilities of Native- and Foreign-Born Persons According to the *Encyclopedia Britannica Almanac 2006*, the 2004 U.S. population of 288,280,000 included 34,244,000 who were foreign born. Find the empirical probability that a randomly chosen person of that population would be .
(a) foreign born
(b) native born.

16. *Probabilities of Two Daughters Among Four Children*
In Example 3, what would be Michelle's probability of having exactly two daughters if she were to have four children altogether? (You may want to use a tree diagram to construct the sample space.)

17. Explain the difference between theoretical and empirical probability.

18. Explain the difference between probability and odds.

Genetics in Snapdragons Mendel found no dominance in snapdragons (in contrast to peas) with respect to red and white flower color. When pure red and pure white parents are crossed (see Table 2), the resulting Rr *combination (one of each gene) produces second-generation offspring with* pink *flowers. These second-generation pinks, however, still carry one red and one white gene, so when they are crossed the third generation is still governed by Table 3.*

Find each probability for third-generation snapdragons.

19. *P*(red)   **20.** *P*(pink)   **21.** *P*(white)

Genetics in Pea Plants Mendel also investigated various characteristics besides flower color. For example, round peas are dominant over recessive wrinkled peas. First, second, and third generations can again be analyzed using Tables 2 and 3, where R *represents round and* r *represents wrinkled.*

22. Explain why crossing pure round and pure wrinkled first-generation parents will always produce round peas in the second-generation offspring.

23. When second-generation round pea plants (each of which carries both R and r genes) are crossed, find the probability that a third-generation offspring will have
(a) round peas   **(b)** wrinkled peas.

Genetics of Cystic Fibrosis Cystic fibrosis is one of the most common inherited diseases in North America (including the United States), occurring in about 1 of every 2000 Caucasian births and about 1 of every 250,000 non-Caucasian births. Even with modern treatment, victims usually die from lung damage by their early twenties.

If we denote a cystic fibrosis gene with a c and a disease-free gene with a C (since the disease is recessive), then only a cc person will actually have the disease. Such persons would ordinarily die before parenting children, but a child can also inherit the disease from two Cc parents (who themselves are healthy, that is, have no symptoms but are "carriers" of the disease). This is like a

pea plant inheriting white flowers from two red-flowered parents which both carry genes for white.

24. Find the empirical probability (to four decimal places) that cystic fibrosis will occur in a randomly selected infant birth among U.S. Caucasians.

25. Find the empirical probability (to six decimal places) that cystic fibrosis will occur in a randomly selected infant birth among U.S. non-Caucasians.

26. Among 150,000 North American Caucasian births, about how many occurrences of cystic fibrosis would you expect?

Suppose that both partners in a marriage are cystic fibrosis carriers (a rare occurrence). Construct a chart similar to Table 3 and determine the probability of each of the following events.

27. Their first child will have the disease.

28. Their first child will be a carrier.

29. Their first child will neither have nor carry the disease.

Suppose a child is born to one cystic fibrosis carrier parent and one non-carrier parent. Find the probability of each of the following events.

30. The child will have cystic fibrosis.

31. The child will be a healthy cystic fibrosis carrier.

32. The child will neither have nor carry the disease.

Genetics of Sickle-Cell Anemia Sickle-cell anemia occurs in about 1 of every 500 black baby births and about 1 of every 160,000 non-black baby births. It is ordinarily fatal in early childhood. There is a test to identify carriers. Unlike cystic fibrosis, which is recessive, sickle-cell anemia is **codominant.** *This means that inheriting two sickle-cell genes causes the disease, while inheriting just one sickle-cell gene causes a mild (non-fatal) version (which is called* **sickle-cell trait**). *This is similar to a snapdragon plant manifesting pink flowers by inheriting one red gene and one white gene.*

In Exercises 33 and 34, find the empirical probabilities of the given events.

33. A randomly selected black baby will have sickle-cell anemia. (Give your answer to three decimal places.)

34. A randomly selected non-black baby will have sickle-cell anemia. (Give your answer to six decimal places.)

35. Among 80,000 births of black babies, about how many occurrences of sickle-cell anemia would you expect?

Find the theoretical probability of each condition in a child both of whose parents have sickle-cell trait.

36. The child will have sickle-cell anemia.

37. The child will have sickle-cell trait.

38. The child will be healthy.

39. ***Women's 100-Meter Run*** In the history of track and field, no woman has broken the 10-second barrier in the 100-meter run.

 (a) From the statement above, find the empirical probability that a woman runner will break the 10-second barrier next year.
 (b) Can you find the theoretical probability for the event of part (a)?
 (c) Is it possible that the event of part (a) will occur?

40. Is there any way a coin could fail to be "fair"? Explain.

41. On page 27 of their book *Descartes' Dream,* Philip Davis and Reuben Hersh ask the question, "Is probability real or is it just a cover-up for ignorance?" What do you think? Are some things truly random, or is everything potentially deterministic?

42. If $P(E) = .37$, find
 (a) the odds in favor of E,
 (b) the odds against E.

43. If the odds in favor of event E are 12 to 19, find $P(E)$.

44. If the odds against event E are 10 to 3, find $P(E)$.

Probabilities of Poker Hands *In 5-card poker, find the probability of being dealt each of the following. Give each answer to eight decimal places. (Refer to Table 1.)*

45. a straight flush

46. two pairs

47. four of a kind

48. four queens

49. a hearts flush (*not* a royal flush or a straight flush)

50. ***Probabilities in Dart Throwing*** If a dart hits the square target shown here at random, what is the probability that it will hit in a colored region? (*Hint:* Compare the area of the colored regions to the total area of the target.)

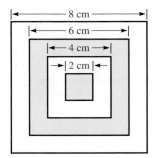

51. ***Probabilities in Olympic Curling*** In the Olympic event of curling, the scoring area (shown here) consists of four concentric circles on the ice with radii of 6 inches, 2 feet, 4 feet, and 6 feet.

If a team member lands a (43-pound) stone *randomly* within the scoring area, find the probability that it ends up centered on
 (a) red (b) white (c) blue.

52. *Drawing Cards* When drawing cards without replacement from a standard 52-card deck, find the maximum number of cards you could possibly draw and still get
(a) fewer than three black cards,
(b) fewer than six spades,
(c) fewer than four face cards,
(d) fewer than two kings.

The remaining exercises require careful thought to determine $n(E)$ and $n(S)$. (In some cases, you may want to employ counting methods from Chapter 1, such as the fundamental counting principle, permutations, or combinations.)

Probabilities of Seating Arrangements *Three married couples arrange themselves randomly in six consecutive seats in a row. Find the probability of each event in Exercises 53–56. (Hint: In each case the denominator of the probability fraction will be $6! = 720$, the total number of ways to arrange six items.)*

53. Each man will sit immediately to the left of his wife.

54. Each man will sit immediately to the left of a woman.

55. The women will be in three adjacent seats.

56. The women will be in three adjacent seats, as will the men.

57. *Selecting Slopes* If two distinct numbers are chosen randomly from the set $\{-2, -\frac{4}{3}, -\frac{1}{2}, 0, \frac{1}{2}, \frac{3}{4}, 3\}$, find the probability that they will be the slopes of two perpendicular lines.

58. *Racing Bets* At most horse-racing tracks, the "trifecta" is a particular race where you win if you correctly pick the "win," "place," and "show" horses (the first-, second-, and third-place winners), in their proper order. If five horses of equal ability are entered in today's trifecta race, and you select an entry, what is the probability that you will be a winner?

59. *Probabilities of Student Course Schedules* Suppose you plan to take three courses next term. If you select them randomly from a listing of twelve courses, five of which are science courses, what is the probability that all three courses you select will be science courses?

60. *Selecting Symphony Performances* Cheryl Chechvala randomly selects three symphony performances to attend this season, choosing from a schedule of ten performances, three of which will feature works by Beethoven. Find the probability that Cheryl will select all of the Beethoven programs.

Selecting Class Reports *Assuming that Ben, Jill, and Pam are three of the 36 members of the class, and that three of the class members will be chosen randomly to deliver their reports during the next class meeting, find the probability (to six decimal places) of each event.*

61. Ben, Jill, and Pam are selected, in that order.

62. Ben, Jill, and Pam are selected, in any order.

63. *Random Selection of Prime Numbers* If two distinct prime numbers are randomly selected from among the first eight prime numbers, what is the probability that their sum will be 24?

64. *Building Numbers from Sets of Digits* The digits 1, 2, 3, 4, and 5 are randomly arranged to form a five-digit number. Find the probability of each of the following events.
(a) The number is even.
(b) The first and last digits of the number both are even.

65. *Random Sums* Two integers are randomly selected from the set $\{1, 2, 3, 4, 5, 6, 7, 8, 9\}$ and are added together. Find the probability that their sum is 11 if they are selected
(a) with replacement
(b) without replacement.

Finding Palindromic Numbers *Numbers that are **palindromes** read the same forward and backward. For example, 30203 is a five-digit palindrome. If a single number is chosen randomly from each of the following sets, find the probability that it will be palindromic.*

66. the set of all two-digit numbers

67. the set of all three-digit numbers

2.2 Events Involving "Not" and "Or"

Properties of Probability • Events Involving "Not" • Events Involving "Or"

Pierre Simon de Laplace
(1749–1827) began in 1773 to solve the problem of why Jupiter's orbit seems to shrink and Saturn's orbit seems to expand. Eventually Laplace worked out a complete theory of the solar system. *Celestial Mechanics* resulted from almost a lifetime of work. In five volumes, it was published between 1799 and 1825 and gained for Laplace the reputation "Newton of France."

Laplace's work on probability was actually an adjunct to his celestial mechanics. He needed to demonstrate that probability is useful in interpreting scientific data. He also wrote a popular exposition of the system, which contains (in a footnote!) the "nebular hypothesis" that the sun and planets originated together in a cloud of matter, which then cooled and condensed into separate bodies.

Properties of Probability Remember from the previous section that an empirical probability, based upon experimental observation, may be the best value available but still is only an approximation to the ("true") theoretical probability. For example, no human has ever been known to jump higher than 8.5 feet vertically, so the empirical probability of such an event is zero. However, observing the rate at which high jump records have been broken, we suspect that the event is, in fact, possible and may one day occur. Hence it must have some nonzero theoretical probability, even though we have no way of assessing its exact value.

Recall also that the theoretical probability formula,

$$P(E) = \frac{n(E)}{n(S)},$$

is valid only when all outcomes in the sample space S are equally likely. For the experiment of tossing two fair coins, we can write $S = \{hh, ht, th, tt\}$ and compute correctly that

$$P(\text{both heads}) = \frac{1}{4},$$

whereas if we define the sample space with non-equally likely outcomes as $S = \{\text{both heads, both tails, one of each}\}$, we are led to

$$P(\text{both heads}) = \frac{1}{3}, \qquad \text{which is } wrong.$$

(To convince yourself that $\frac{1}{4}$ is a better value than $\frac{1}{3}$, toss two fair coins 100 times or so to see what the empirical fraction seems to approach.)

Since any event E is a subset of the sample space S, we know that $0 \leq n(E) \leq n(S)$. Dividing all members of this inequality by $n(S)$ gives

$$\frac{0}{n(S)} \leq \frac{n(E)}{n(S)} \leq \frac{n(S)}{n(S)}, \quad \text{or} \quad \mathbf{0 \leq P(E) \leq 1.}$$

In words, the probability of any event is a number from 0 through 1, inclusive.

If event E is *impossible* (cannot happen), then $n(E)$ must be 0 (E is the empty set), so $P(E) = 0$. If event E is *certain* (cannot help but happen), then $n(E) = n(S)$, so $P(E) = \frac{n(E)}{n(S)} = \frac{n(S)}{n(S)} = 1$. These properties are summarized below.

Properties of Probability

Let E be an event from the sample space S. That is, E is a subset of S. Then the following properties hold.

1. $\mathbf{0 \leq P(E) \leq 1}$ (The probability of an event is a number from 0 through 1, inclusive.)
2. $\mathbf{P(\emptyset) = 0}$ (The probability of an impossible event is 0.)
3. $\mathbf{P(S) = 1}$ (The probability of a certain event is 1.)

EXAMPLE 1   Finding Probability When Rolling a Die

When a single fair die is rolled, find the probability of each event.

(a) the number 2 is rolled   **(b)** a number other than 2 is rolled
(c) the number 7 is rolled   **(d)** a number less than 7 is rolled

SOLUTION

(a) Since one of the six possibilities is a 2, $P(2) = \frac{1}{6}$.
(b) There are five such numbers, 1, 3, 4, 5, and 6, so $P(\text{a number other than 2}) = \frac{5}{6}$.
(c) None of the possible outcomes is 7. Thus, $P(7) = \frac{0}{6} = 0$.
(d) Since all six of the possible outcomes are less than 7, $P(\text{a number less than }7) = \frac{6}{6} = 1$.

Notice that no probability in Example 1 was less than 0 or greater than 1, which illustrates probability property 1. The "impossible" event of part (c) had probability 0, illustrating property 2. And the "certain" event of part (d) had probability 1, illustrating property 3.

Events Involving "Not"   Table 4 repeats the information of Table 8 of Section 1.5, with a third correspondence added in row 3. These correspondences are the basis for the probability rules developed in this section and the next. For example, the probability of an event *not* happening involves the *complement* and *subtraction*, according to row 1 of the table.

TABLE 4   Set Theory/Logic/Arithmetic Correspondences

	Set Theory	Logic	Arithmetic
1. Operation or Connective (Symbol)	Complement (′)	Not (~)	Subtraction (−)
2. Operation or Connective (Symbol)	Union (∪)	Or (∨)	Addition (+)
3. Operation or Connective (Symbol)	Intersection (∩)	And (∧)	Multiplication (·)

The rule for the probability of a complement is stated as follows. It is illustrated in Figure 4.

> **Probability of a Complement (for Not E)**
>
> The probability that an event E will *not* occur is equal to one minus the probability that it *will* occur.
> $$P(\text{not } E) = 1 - P(E)$$

Notice that the events of Examples 1(a) and (b), namely "2" and "not 2," are complements of one another, and that their probabilities add up to 1. This illustrates the above probability rule. The equation

$$P(E) + P(E') = 1$$

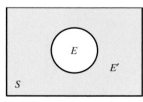

The logical connective "not" corresponds to "complement" in set theory.

$P(not\ E) = P(S) - P(E)$
$\qquad\quad = 1 - P(E)$

FIGURE 4

Mary Somerville (1780–1872) is associated with Laplace because of her brilliant exposition of his *Celestial Mechanics.* She combined a deep understanding of science with the ability to communicate its concepts to the general public.

Somerville studied Euclid thoroughly and perfected her Latin so she could read Newton's *Principia.* In about 1816 she went to London and soon became part of its literary and scientific circles. She also corresponded with Laplace and other Continental scientists.

Somerville's book on Laplace's theories came out in 1831 with great acclaim. Then followed a panoramic book, *Connection of the Physical Sciences* (1834). A statement in one of its editions suggested that irregularities in the orbit of Uranus might indicate that a more remote planet, not yet seen, existed. This caught the eye of the scientists who worked out the calculations for Neptune's orbit.

is a rearrangement of the formula for the probability of a complement. Another form of the equation, also useful at times, is

$$P(E) = 1 - P(E').$$

EXAMPLE 2 Finding the Probability of a Complement

When a single card is drawn from a standard 52-card deck, what is the probability that it will not be a king?

SOLUTION

$$P(\text{not a king}) = 1 - P(\text{king}) = 1 - \frac{4}{52} = \frac{48}{52} = \frac{12}{13}. \longleftarrow$$ Remember to write in lowest terms.

EXAMPLE 3 Finding the Probability of a Complement

If five fair coins are tossed, find the probability of obtaining at least one head.

SOLUTION

There are $2^5 = 32$ possible outcomes for the experiment of tossing five fair coins. Most include at least one head. In fact, only the outcome ttttt does not include at least one head. If E denotes the event "at least one head," then E' is the event "not at least one head," and

$$P(E) = 1 - P(E') = 1 - \frac{1}{32} = \frac{31}{32}.$$

Events Involving "Or"
Examples 2 and 3 showed how the probability of an event can be approached indirectly, by first considering the complement of the event. Another indirect approach is to break the event into simpler component events. Row 2 of Table 4 indicates that the probability of one event *or* another should involve the *union* and *addition.*

EXAMPLE 4 Selecting From a Set of Numbers

If one number is selected randomly from the set {1, 2, 3, 4, 5, 6, 7, 8, 9, 10}, find the probability that it will be

(a) odd or a multiple of 4
(b) odd or a multiple of 3.

SOLUTION

Define the following events:

$$S = \{1, 2, 3, 4, 5, 6, 7, 8, 9, 10\} \quad \text{Sample space}$$
$$A = \{1, 3, 5, 7, 9\} \quad \text{Odd outcomes}$$
$$B = \{4, 8\} \quad \text{Multiples of 4}$$
$$C = \{3, 6, 9\} \quad \text{Multiples of 3}$$

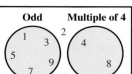

FIGURE 5

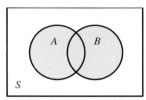

FIGURE 6

(a) Figure 5 shows the positioning of the 10 integers within the sample space and within the pertinent sets A and B. The composite event "A or B" corresponds to the set $A \cup B = \{1, 3, 4, 5, 7, 8, 9\}$. By the theoretical probability formula,

Of 10 total outcomes, 7 are favorable.

$$P(A \text{ or } B) = \frac{7}{10}.$$

(b) Figure 6 shows the situation. We see that

Of 10 total outcomes, 6 are favorable.

$$P(A \text{ or } C) = \frac{6}{10} = \frac{3}{5}.$$

Would an addition formula have worked in Example 4? Let's check. In part (a),

$$P(A \text{ or } B) = P(A) + P(B) = \frac{5}{10} + \frac{2}{10} = \frac{7}{10}, \quad \text{Correct}$$

which is correct. In part (b),

$$P(A \text{ or } C) = P(A) + P(C) = \frac{5}{10} + \frac{3}{10} = \frac{8}{10} = \frac{4}{5}, \quad \text{Incorrect}$$

which is incorrect. The trouble in part (b) is that A and C are not disjoint sets. They have outcomes in common. Just as with the additive counting principle in Chapter 1, an adjustment must be made here to compensate for counting the common outcomes twice. The correct calculation is

$$P(A \text{ or } C) = P(A) + P(C) - P(A \text{ and } C)$$

$$= \frac{5}{10} + \frac{3}{10} - \frac{2}{10} = \frac{6}{10} = \frac{3}{5}. \quad \text{Correct}$$

In probability theory, events that are disjoint sets are called *mutually exclusive events,* which are defined as follows.

The logical connective "or" corresponds to "union" in set theory.

$P(A \text{ or } B)$
$= P(A) + P(B) - P(A \text{ and } B)$

FIGURE 7

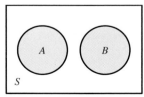

When A and B are mutually exclusive,

$P(A \text{ or } B) = P(A) + P(B).$

FIGURE 8

Mutually Exclusive Events

Two events A and B are **mutually exclusive events** if they have no outcomes in common. (Mutually exclusive events cannot occur simultaneously.)

The results observed in Example 4 are generalized as follows. The two possibilities are illustrated in Figures 7 and 8.

Addition Rule of Probability (for *A* or *B*)

If A and B are any two events, then

$$P(A \text{ or } B) = P(A) + P(B) - P(A \text{ and } B).$$

If **A and B are mutually exclusive,** then

$$P(A \text{ or } B) = P(A) + P(B).$$

Actually, the first formula in the addition rule applies in all cases. (The third term on the right drops out when A and B are mutually exclusive, because $P(A \text{ and } B) = 0$).

Still it is good to remember the second formula in the preceding box for the many cases where the component events are mutually exclusive. In this section, we consider only cases where the event "*A* and *B*" is simple. We deal with more involved composites involving "and" in the next section.

EXAMPLE 5 Finding the Probability of an Event Involving "Or"

If a single card is drawn from a standard 52-card deck, what is the probability that it will be a spade or a red card?

SOLUTION

First note that "spade" and "red" cannot both occur, because there are no red spades. (All spades are black.) Therefore, we can use the formula for mutually exclusive events. With 13 spades and 26 red cards in the deck, we obtain

$$P(\text{spade or red}) = P(\text{spade}) + P(\text{red}) = \frac{13}{52} + \frac{26}{52} = \frac{39}{52} = \frac{3}{4}.$$ ∎

We often need to consider composites of more than two events. When each event involved is mutually exclusive of all the others, we extend the addition rule to the appropriate number of components.

EXAMPLE 6 Treating Unions of Several Components

Jacob will spend from 1 to 6 hours on his homework. If *x* represents the number of hours to be spent, then the probabilities of the various values of *x*, rounded to the nearest hour, are shown in Table 5. Find the probabilities that he will spend

(a) fewer than 3 hours   **(b)** more than 2 hours
(c) more than 1 but no more than 5 hours **(d)** fewer than 5 hours.

SOLUTION

Because the time periods in Table 5 are mutually exclusive of one another, we can simply add the appropriate component probabilities.

(a) $P(\text{fewer than 3}) = P(1 \text{ or } 2)$ Fewer than 3 means 1 or 2.

$\qquad\qquad\qquad\quad = P(1) + P(2)$ Addition rule

$\qquad\qquad\qquad\quad = .05 + .10$ Substitute values from Table 5.

$\qquad\qquad\qquad\quad = .15$

(b) $P(\text{more than 2}) = P(3 \text{ or } 4 \text{ or } 5 \text{ or } 6)$ More than 2 means 3, 4, 5, or 6.

$\qquad\qquad\qquad\quad = P(3) + P(4) + P(5) + P(6)$ Addition rule

$\qquad\qquad\qquad\quad = .20 + .40 + .10 + .15$ Substitute values from Table 5.

$\qquad\qquad\qquad\quad = .85$

(c) $P(\text{more than 1 but no more than 5})$

$\qquad\qquad\qquad\quad = P(2 \text{ or } 3 \text{ or } 4 \text{ or } 5)$ 2, 3, 4, and 5 are more than 1 and no more than 5.

$\qquad\qquad\qquad\quad = P(2) + P(3) + P(4) + P(5)$ Addition rule

$\qquad\qquad\qquad\quad = .10 + .20 + .40 + .10$ Substitute values from Table 5.

$\qquad\qquad\qquad\quad = .80$

TABLE 5

x	P(x)
1	.05
2	.10
3	.20
4	.40
5	.10
6	.15

(d) Although we could take a direct approach here, as in parts (a), (b), and (c), we will combine the complement rule with the addition rule.

$$P(\text{fewer than 5}) = 1 - P(\text{not fewer than 5})$$

Complement rule

$$= 1 - P(\text{5 or more})$$

5 or more is equivalent to not fewer than 5.

$$= 1 - P(\text{5 or 6})$$

5 or more means 5 or 6.

$$= 1 - [P(5) + P(6)]$$

Addition rule

$$= 1 - (.10 + .15)$$

Substitute values from Table 5.

$$= 1 - .25$$

$$= .75$$

Add inside the parentheses first. ■

Table 5, in Example 6, lists all possible time intervals so the corresponding probabilities add up to 1, a necessary condition for the way part (d) was done. The time spent on homework here is an example of a **random variable.** (It is "random" since we cannot predict which of its possible values will occur.) A listing like Table 5, which shows all possible values of a random variable, along with the probabilities that those values will occur, is called a **probability distribution** for that random variable. Since *all* possible values are listed, they make up the entire sample space, and so the listed probabilities must add up to 1 (by probability property 3). Probability distributions will occur in Exercises 32 and 33 of this section and will be discussed further in later sections.

EXAMPLE 7   Finding the Probability of an Event Involving "Or"

Find the probability that a single card drawn from a standard 52-card deck will be a diamond or a face card.

SOLUTION

In this case, the component events "diamond" and "face card" can both occur. (The jack, queen, and king of diamonds belong to both.) So, we must use the first formula of the addition rule. If D denotes "diamond" and F denotes "face card," we obtain

$$P(D \text{ or } F) = P(D) + P(F) - P(D \text{ and } F)$$

Addition rule

$$= \frac{13}{52} + \frac{12}{52} - \frac{3}{52}$$

There are 13 diamonds, 12 face cards, and 3 that are both.

$$= \frac{22}{52}$$

Add and subtract.

$$= \frac{11}{26}.$$

Write in lowest terms. ■

EXAMPLE 8   Finding the Probability of an Event Involving "Or"

Of 20 elective courses to be offered this term, Juanita plans to enroll in one, which she will choose by throwing a dart at the schedule of courses. If 8 of the courses are recreational, 9 are interesting, and 3 are both recreational and interesting, find the probability that the course she chooses will have at least one of these two attributes.

SOLUTION

If R denotes "recreational" and I denotes "interesting," then $P(R) = \frac{8}{20}$, $P(I) = \frac{9}{20}$, and $P(R \text{ and } I) = \frac{3}{20}$. Because R and I are not mutually exclusive, we use the formula for that case.

$$P(R \text{ or } I) = \frac{8}{20} + \frac{9}{20} - \frac{3}{20} = \frac{14}{20} = \frac{7}{10}.$$

Remember to write in lowest terms. ■

2.2 EXERCISES

1. ***Determining Whether Two Events Are Mutually Exclusive*** Julie Davis has three office assistants. If A is the event that at least two of them are men and B is the event that at least two of them are women, are A and B mutually exclusive?

2. ***Attending Different Colleges*** Nancy Hart earned her college degree several years ago. Consider the following four events.

   Her alma mater is in the East.

   Her alma mater is a private college.

   Her alma mater is in the Northwest.

   Her alma mater is in the South.

   Are these events all mutually exclusive of one another?

3. Explain the difference between the two formulas in the addition rule of probability on page 69, illustrating each one with an appropriate example.

Probabilities for Rolling a Die *For the experiment of rolling a single fair die, find the probability of each event.*

4. not less than 2

5. not prime

6. odd or less than 5

7. even or prime

8. odd or even

9. less than 3 or greater than 4

Probability and Odds for Drawing a Card *For the experiment of drawing a single card from a standard 52-card deck, find* **(a)** *the probability, and* **(b)** *the odds in favor, of each event.*

10. not an ace

11. king or queen

12. club or heart

13. spade or face card

14. not a heart, or a 7

15. neither a heart nor a 7

Number Sums for Rolling a Pair of Dice *For the experiment of rolling an ordinary pair of dice, find the probability that the sum will be each of the following. (You may want to use a table showing the sum for each of the 36 equally likely outcomes.)*

16. 11 or 12

17. even or a multiple of 3

18. odd or greater than 9

19. less than 3 or greater than 9

20. Find the probability of getting a prime number in each case.
   (a) A number is chosen randomly from the set $\{1, 2, 3, 4, \ldots, 12\}$.
   (b) Two dice are rolled and the sum is observed.

21. Suppose, for a given experiment, A, B, C, and D are events, all mutually exclusive of one another, such that $A \cup B \cup C \cup D = S$ (the sample space). By extending the addition rule of probability on page 69 to this case, and utilizing probability property 3, what statement can you make?

Probabilities of Poker Hands *If you are dealt a 5-card hand (this implies without replacement) from a standard 52-card deck, find the probability of getting each of the following. Refer to Table 1 of Section 2.1, and give answers to six decimal places.*

22. a flush or three of a kind

23. a full house or a straight

24. a black flush or two pairs

25. nothing any better than two pairs

Probabilities in Golf Scoring *The table gives golfer Amy Donlin's probabilities of scoring in various ranges on a par-70 course. In a given round, find the probability of each event in Exercises 26–30.*

x	$P(x)$
Below 60	.04
60–64	.06
65–69	.14
70–74	.30
75–79	.23
80–84	.09
85–89	.06
90–94	.04
95–99	.03
100 or above	.01

26. 95 or higher

27. par or above

28. in the 80s

29. less than 90

30. not in the 70s, 80s, or 90s

31. What are the odds of Amy's shooting below par?

32. ***Drawing Balls from an Urn*** Anne Kelly randomly chooses a single ball from the urn shown here, and x represents the color of the ball chosen. Construct a complete probability distribution for the random variable x.

33. Let x denote the sum of two distinct numbers selected randomly from the set $\{1, 2, 3, 4, 5\}$. Construct the probability distribution for the random variable x.

34. ***Comparing Empirical and Theoretical Probabilities for Rolling Dice*** Roll a pair of dice 50 times, keeping track of the number of times the sum is "less than 3 or greater than 9" (that is 2, 10, 11, or 12).
   (a) From your results, calculate an empirical probability for the event "less than 3 or greater than 9."
   (b) By how much does your answer differ from the *theoretical* probability of Exercise 19?

For Exercises 35–38, let A be an event within the sample space S, and let n(A) = a and n(S) = s.

35. Use the complements principle of counting to find an expression for $n(A')$.

36. Use the theoretical probability formula to express $P(A)$ and $P(A')$.

37. Evaluate, and simplify, $P(A) + P(A')$.

38. What rule have you proved?

The remaining exercises require careful thought for the determination of n(E) and n(S). (In some cases, you may want to employ counting methods from Chapter 1, such as the fundamental counting principle, permutations, or combinations.)

Building Numbers from Sets of Digits *Suppose we want to form three-digit numbers using the set of digits* $\{0, 1, 2, 3, 4, 5\}$. *For example,* 501 *and* 224 *are such numbers but* 035 *is not.*

39. How many such numbers are possible?

40. How many of these numbers are multiples of 5?

41. If one three-digit number is chosen at random from all those that can be made from the above set of digits, find the probability that the one chosen is not a multiple of 5.

42. ***Multiplying Numbers Generated by Spinners*** An experiment consists of spinning both spinners shown here and multiplying the resulting numbers together. Find the probability that the resulting product will be even.

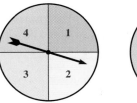 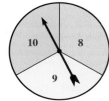

43. ***Drawing Colored Marbles from Boxes*** A bag contains fifty blue and fifty green marbles. Two marbles at a time are randomly selected. If both are green, they are placed in box A; if both are blue, in box B; if one is green and the other is blue, in box C. After all marbles are drawn, what is the probability that the numbers of marbles in box A and box B are the same? (This problem is borrowed with permission from the December 1992 issue of *Mathematics Teacher,* page 736.)

2.3 Conditional Probability; Events Involving "And"

Conditional Probability • Events Involving "And"

Even **a rare occurrence** can sometimes cause widespread controversy. When Mattel Toys marketed a new talking Barbie doll a few years ago, some of the Barbies were programmed to say "Math class is tough." The National Council of Teachers of Mathematics (NCTM), the American Association of University Women (AAUW), and numerous consumers voiced complaints about the damage such a message could do to the self-confidence of children and to their attitudes toward school and mathematics. Mattel subsequently agreed to erase the phrase from the microchip to be used in future doll production.

Incidentally, each Barbie was programmed to say four different statements, randomly selected from a pool of 270 prerecorded statements. Therefore, the probability of getting one that said "Math class is tough" was only

$$\frac{1 \cdot {}_{269}C_3}{{}_{270}C_4} \approx .015.$$

Other messages included in the pool were "I love school, don't you?," "I'm studying to be a doctor," and "Let's study for the quiz."

Conditional Probability Sometimes the probability of an event must be computed using the knowledge that some other event has happened (or is happening, or will happen—the timing is not important). This type of probability is called *conditional probability*.

Conditional Probability

The probability of event B, computed on the assumption that event A has happened, is called the **conditional probability of B, given A,** and is denoted $P(B \mid A)$.

▇ EXAMPLE 1 Selecting from a Set of Numbers

From the sample space $S = \{1, 2, 3, 4, 5, 6, 7, 8, 9, 10\}$, a single number is to be selected randomly. Given the events

   A: The selected number is odd,   and B: The selected number is a multiple of 3,

find each probability.

(a) $P(B)$ **(b)** $P(A \text{ and } B)$ **(c)** $P(B \mid A)$

SOLUTION

(a) $B = \{3, 6, 9\}$, so $P(B) = \frac{n(B)}{n(S)} = \frac{3}{10}$.

(b) A and B is the set $A \cap B = \{1, 3, 5, 7, 9\} \cap \{3, 6, 9\} = \{3, 9\}$, so

$$P(A \text{ and } B) = \frac{n(A \cap B)}{n(S)} = \frac{2}{10} = \frac{1}{5}.$$

(c) The given condition, that A occurs, effectively reduces the sample space from S to A, and the elements of the new sample space A, that are also in B, are the elements of $A \cap B$. Therefore,

$$P(B \mid A) = \frac{n(A \cap B)}{n(A)} = \frac{2}{5}.$$ ▇

Example 1 illustrates some important points. First, because

$$\frac{n(A \cap B)}{n(A)} = \frac{\dfrac{n(A \cap B)}{n(S)}}{\dfrac{n(A)}{n(S)}} \qquad \text{Multiply numerator and denominator by } \tfrac{1}{n(S)}.$$

$$= \frac{P(A \cap B)}{P(A)}, \qquad \text{Theoretical probability formula}$$

the final line of the example gives the following convenient formula for computing conditional probability, which works in all cases.

Natural disasters, such as tornadoes and cyclones, earthquakes, tsunamis, volcanic eruptions, firestorms, and floods, can kill thousands of people. But a **cosmic impact,** the collision of a meteor, comet, or asteroid with Earth, could be at least as catastrophic as full-scale nuclear war, killing a billion or more people. Reported at the Web site www.impact.arc.nasa.gov is that a large enough object (1 kilometer or more in diameter) could even put the human species at risk of annihilation by causing drastic climate changes and destroying food crops. By the end of 2004, the Spaceguard Survey had already discovered more than half of the near-Earth asteroids (NEAs) in this size range and had plans to locate 90% of them by the end of 2008.

Although the risk of finding one on a collision course with the Earth is slight, it is anticipated that, if we did, we would be able to deflect it before impact.

The photo above shows damage caused by a cosmic fragment that disintegrated in the atmosphere over Tunguska, Siberia, in 1908, with an explosive energy of more than 10 megatons of TNT. Nearly 1000 square miles of uninhabited forest were flattened.

Conditional Probability Formula

The **conditional probability of B, given A,** is given by

$$P(B \mid A) = \frac{P(A \cap B)}{P(A)} = \frac{P(A \text{ and } B)}{P(A)}.$$

A second observation from Example 1 is that the conditional probability of B, given A, was $\frac{2}{5}$, whereas the "unconditional" probability of B (with no condition given) was $\frac{3}{10}$, so the condition did make a difference.

EXAMPLE 2 Finding Probabilities of Boys and Girls in a Family

Given a family with two children, find the probabilities that

(a) both are girls, given that at least one is a girl, and
(b) both are girls, given that the older child is a girl.

(Assume boys and girls are equally likely.)

SOLUTION

We define the following events.

$$S = \{gg, gb, bg, bb\} \quad \text{The sample space}$$
$$A = \{gg\} \quad \text{Both are girls.}$$
$$B = \{gg, gb, bg\} \quad \text{At least one is a girl.}$$
$$C = \{gg, gb\} \quad \text{The older one is a girl.}$$

Note that $A \cap B = \{gg\}$.

(a) $P(A \mid B) = \dfrac{P(A \text{ and } B)}{P(B)} = \dfrac{\frac{1}{4}}{\frac{3}{4}} = \dfrac{1}{4} \div \dfrac{3}{4} = \dfrac{1}{4} \cdot \dfrac{4}{3} = \dfrac{1}{3}$

(b) $P(A \mid C) = \dfrac{P(A \text{ and } C)}{P(C)} = \dfrac{\frac{1}{4}}{\frac{2}{4}} = \dfrac{1}{4} \div \dfrac{2}{4} = \dfrac{1}{4} \cdot \dfrac{4}{2} = \dfrac{1}{2}$

We noted earlier that in Example 1, the condition A did affect the value of $P(B)$. However, sometimes a conditional probability is no different than the corresponding unconditional probability, in which case we call the two events *independent*. Independent events are defined generally as follows.

Independent Events

Two events A and B are called **independent events** if knowledge about the occurrence of one of them has no effect on the probability of the other one, that is, if

$$P(B \mid A) = P(B), \quad \text{or, equivalently,} \quad P(A \mid B) = P(A).$$

EXAMPLE 3 Checking Events for Independence

A single card is to be drawn from a standard 52-card deck. (The sample space S has 52 elements.) Given the events

A: The selected card is a face card,   and B: The selected card is black,

(a) Find $P(B)$.   **(b)** Find $P(B|A)$.
(c) Determine whether events A and B are independent.

SOLUTION

(a) There are 26 black cards in the 52-card deck, so

$$P(B) = \frac{26}{52} = \frac{1}{2}. \quad \text{Theoretical probability formula}$$

(b) $P(B|A) = \dfrac{P(B \text{ and } A)}{P(A)}$ Conditional probability formula

$$= \frac{\frac{6}{52}}{\frac{12}{52}} \quad \text{Of 52 cards, 12 are face cards and 6 are black face cards.}$$

$$= \frac{6}{52} \cdot \frac{52}{12} = \frac{1}{2} \quad \text{Calculate and write in lowest terms.}$$

(c) Because $P(B|A) = P(B)$, events A and B are independent. ■

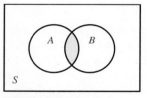

The logical connective "and" corresponds to "intersection" in set theory.

$P(A \text{ and } B) = P(A) \cdot P(B|A)$

FIGURE 9

Events Involving "And"   If we multiply both sides of the conditional probability formula by $P(A)$, we obtain an expression for $P(A \cap B)$, which applies to events of the form "A and B." The resulting formula is related to the fundamental counting principle of Chapter 1. It is illustrated in Figure 9. Just as the calculation of $P(A \text{ or } B)$ is simpler when A and B are mutually exclusive, the calculation of $P(A \text{ and } B)$ is simpler when A and B are independent.

> **Multiplication Rule of Probability (for A and B)**
>
> If A and B are any two events, then
>
> $$P(A \text{ and } B) = P(A) \cdot P(B|A).$$
>
> If A and B are independent, then
>
> $$P(A \text{ and } B) = P(A) \cdot P(B).$$

The first formula in the multiplication rule actually applies in all cases. ($P(B|A) = P(B)$ when A and B are independent.) Still, the independence of the component events is clear in many cases, so it is good to remember the second formula as well.

EXAMPLE 4 Selecting from a Set of Books

Each year, Diane Carr adds to her book collection a number of new publications that she believes will be of lasting value and interest. She has categorized each of her twenty acquisitions for 2007 as hardcover or paperback and as fiction or nonfiction. The numbers of books in the various categories are shown in Table 6.

TABLE 6 Year 2007 Books

	Fiction (*F*)	Nonfiction (*N*)	Totals
Hardcover (*H*)	3	5	8
Paperback (*P*)	8	4	12
Totals	11	9	20

If Diane randomly chooses one of these 20 books, find the probability it will be

(a) hardcover, **(b)** fiction, given it is hardcover, **(c)** hardcover and fiction.

SOLUTION

(a) Eight of the 20 books are hardcover, so $P(H) = \frac{8}{20} = \frac{2}{5}$.

(b) The given condition that the book is hardcover reduces the sample space to eight books. Of those eight, just three are fiction, so $P(F\,|\,H) = \frac{3}{8}$.

(c) $P(H \text{ and } F) = P(H) \cdot P(F\,|\,H) = \frac{2}{5} \cdot \frac{3}{8} = \frac{3}{20}$ Multiplication rule

It is easier here if we simply notice, directly from Table 6, that 3 of the 20 books are "hardcover and fiction." This verifies that the general multiplication rule of probability did give us the correct answer. ▪

EXAMPLE 5   Selecting from a Set of Planets

Table 7 lists the nine generally acknowledged planets of our solar system (prior to 2006)* together with their mean distances from the sun, in millions of kilometers. (Data is from the *Time Almanac 1999*.) Selina must choose two distinct planets to cover in her astronomy report. If she selects randomly, find the probability that the first one selected is closer to the sun than Mars and the second is closer than Saturn.

SOLUTION

We define the events

   A: The first is closer than Mars,   and   *B*: The second is closer than Saturn.

Then $P(A) = \frac{3}{9} = \frac{1}{3}$. (Three of the original nine choices are favorable.) If the planet selected first is closer than Mars, it is also closer than Saturn, and since that planet is no longer available, $P(B\,|\,A) = \frac{4}{8} = \frac{1}{2}$. (Four of the remaining eight are favorable.) The desired probability is

$$P(A \text{ and } B) = P(A) \cdot P(B\,|\,A) = \frac{1}{3} \cdot \frac{1}{2} = \frac{1}{6} \approx .167. \quad \text{Multiplication rule}$$ ▪

In Example 5, the condition that *A* had occurred changed the probability of *B*, since the selection was done, in effect, without replacement. (Repetitions were not allowed.) Events *A* and *B* were not independent. On the other hand, in the next example, the same events, *A* and *B*, will be independent.

TABLE 7

Mean Distance of Planets* from the Sun

Mercury	57.9
Venus	108.2
Earth	149.6
Mars	227.9
Jupiter	778.3
Saturn	1427
Uranus	2870
Neptune	4497
Pluto	5900

*In 2006, Pluto was officially downgraded from "planet" status.

EXAMPLE 6 Selecting from a Set of Planets

Selina must again select two planets, but this time one is for an oral report, the other is for a written report, and they need not be distinct. (The same planet may be selected for both.) Again find the probability that, if she selects randomly, the first is closer than Mars and the second is closer than Saturn.

SOLUTION

Defining events A and B as in Example 5, we have $P(A) = \frac{3}{9} = \frac{1}{3}$, just as before. But the selection is now done *with* replacement. Repetitions *are* allowed. In this case event B is independent of event A, so we can use the second form of the multiplication rule, obtaining a different answer than in Example 5.

$$P(A \text{ and } B) = P(A) \cdot P(B) = \frac{1}{3} \cdot \frac{5}{9} = \frac{5}{27} \approx .185$$

EXAMPLE 7 Selecting from a Deck of Cards

A single card is drawn from a standard 52-card deck. Let B denote the event that the card is black, and let D denote the event that it is a diamond. Answer each question.

(a) Are events B and D independent?   **(b)** Are events B and D mutually exclusive?

SOLUTION

(a) For the unconditional probability of D, we get $P(D) = \frac{13}{52} = \frac{1}{4}$. (Thirteen of the 52 cards are diamonds.) But for the conditional probability of D, given B, we have $P(D|B) = \frac{0}{26} = 0$. (None of the 26 black cards are diamonds.) Since the conditional probability $P(D|B)$ is different than the unconditional probability $P(D)$, B and D are not independent.

(b) Mutually exclusive events, defined in the previous section, are events that cannot both occur for a given performance of an experiment. Since no card in the deck is both black and a diamond, B and D are mutually exclusive.

(People sometimes get the idea that "mutually exclusive" and "independent" mean the same thing. This example shows that this is not so.)

The multiplication rule of probability, can be extended to cases where more than two events are involved.

EXAMPLE 8 Selecting from an Urn of Balls

Anne is still drawing balls from the same urn (shown at the side). This time she draws three balls, without replacement. Find the probability that she gets red, yellow, and blue balls, in that order.

SOLUTION

Using appropriate letters to denote the colors, and subscripts to indicate first, second, and third draws, the event can be symbolized R_1 and Y_2 and B_3, so

$$P(R_1 \text{ and } Y_2 \text{ and } B_3) = P(R_1) \cdot P(Y_2|R_1) \cdot P(B_3|R_1 \text{ and } Y_2)$$

$$= \frac{4}{11} \cdot \frac{5}{10} \cdot \frac{2}{9} = \frac{4}{99} \approx .0404.$$

The **search for extraterrestrial intelligence (SETI)** may have begun in earnest as early as 1961 when Dr. Frank Drake presented an equation for estimating the number of possible civilizations in the Milky Way galaxy whose communications we might detect. Over the years, the effort has been advanced by many scientists, including the late astronomer and exobiologist Carl Sagan, who popularized the issue in TV appearances and in his book *The Cosmic Connection: An Extraterrestrial Perspective* (Dell Paperback). "There must be other starfolk," said Sagan. In fact, some astronomers have estimated the odds against life on Earth being the only life in the universe at one hundred billion billion to one.

Other experts disagree. Freeman Dyson, a noted mathematical physicist and astronomer, says in his book *Disturbing the Universe* that after considering the same evidence and arguments, he believes it is just as likely as not (even odds) that there never was any other intelligent life out there.

EXAMPLE 9   Selecting from a Deck of Cards

If five cards are drawn without replacement from a standard 52-card deck, find the probability that they all are hearts.

SOLUTION

Each time a heart is drawn, the number of available cards decreases by one and the number of hearts decreases by one. The probability of drawing only hearts is

$$\frac{13}{52} \cdot \frac{12}{51} \cdot \frac{11}{50} \cdot \frac{10}{49} \cdot \frac{9}{48} = \frac{33}{66,640} \approx .000495.$$

If you studied counting methods (Chapter 1), you may prefer to solve the problem of Example 9 by using the theoretical probability formula and combinations. The total possible number of 5-card hands, drawn without replacement, is $_{52}C_5$, and the number of those containing only hearts is $_{13}C_5$, so the required probability is

$$\frac{_{13}C_5}{_{52}C_5} = \frac{\dfrac{13!}{5!8!}}{\dfrac{52!}{5!47!}} \approx .000495. \quad \text{Use a calculator.}$$

EXAMPLE 10   Using Both Addition and Multiplication Rules

The local garage employs two mechanics, Alex and Ben. Your consumer club has found that Alex does twice as many jobs as Ben, Alex does a good job three out of four times, and Ben does a good job only two out of five times. If you plan to take your car in for repairs, find the probability that a good job will be done.

SOLUTION

We define the events

> A: work done by Alex; B: work done by Ben; G: good job done.

Since Alex does twice as many jobs as Ben, the (unconditional) probabilities of events A and B are, respectively, $\frac{2}{3}$ and $\frac{1}{3}$. Since Alex does a good job three out of four times, the probability of a good job, given that Alex did the work, is $\frac{3}{4}$. And since Ben does well two out of five times, the probability of a good job, given that Ben did the work, is $\frac{2}{5}$. (These last two probabilities are conditional.) These four values can be summarized as

$$P(A) = \frac{2}{3}, \quad P(B) = \frac{1}{3}, \quad P(G|A) = \frac{3}{4}, \quad \text{and} \quad P(G|B) = \frac{2}{5}.$$

Event G can occur in two mutually exclusive ways: Alex could do the work and do a good job ($A \cap G$), or Ben could do the work and do a good job ($B \cap G$). Thus,

$$P(G) = P(A \cap G) + P(B \cap G) \qquad \text{Addition rule}$$
$$= P(A) \cdot P(G|A) + P(B) \cdot P(G|B) \qquad \text{Multiplication rule}$$
$$= \frac{2}{3} \cdot \frac{3}{4} + \frac{1}{3} \cdot \frac{2}{5} \qquad \text{Substitute the values.}$$

Multiply first, then add.

$$= \frac{1}{2} + \frac{2}{15} = \frac{19}{30} \approx .633.$$

The tree diagram in Figure 10 shows a graphical way to organize the work of Example 10. Use the given information to draw the tree diagram, then find the probability of a good job by adding the probabilities from the indicated branches of the tree.

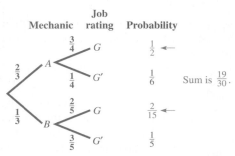

Garage mechanics experiment

FIGURE 10

EXAMPLE 11 Selecting Door Prizes

Michael Bolinder is among five door prize winners at a Christmas party. The five winners are asked to choose, without looking, from a bag which, they are told, contains five tokens, four of them redeemable for candy canes and one specific token redeemable for a $100 gift certificate. Can Michael improve his chance of getting the gift certificate by drawing first among the five people?

SOLUTION

We denote candy cane by C, gift certificate by G, and first draw, second draw, and so on by subscripts $1, 2, \ldots$. Then if Michael draws first, his probability of getting the gift certificate is

$$P(G_1) = \frac{1}{5}.$$

If he draws second, his probability of getting the gift certificate is

$$\begin{aligned} P(G_2) &= P(C_1 \text{ and } G_2) \\ &= P(C_1) \cdot P(G_2 | C_1) \\ &= \frac{4}{5} \cdot \frac{1}{4} = \frac{1}{5}. \quad \text{Same result as above} \end{aligned}$$

For the third draw,

$$\begin{aligned} P(G_3) &= P(C_1 \text{ and } C_2 \text{ and } G_3) \\ &= P(C_1) \cdot P(C_2 | C_1) \cdot P(G_3 | C_1 \text{ and } C_2) \\ &= \frac{4}{5} \cdot \frac{3}{4} \cdot \frac{1}{3} = \frac{1}{5}. \quad \text{Same result as above} \end{aligned}$$

Likewise, the probability of getting the gift certificate is $\frac{1}{5}$ when drawing fourth or when drawing fifth. Therefore, the order in which the five winners draw does not affect Michael's chances. ■

Since 1999, the **search for extraterrestrial intelligence (SETI)** has been carried out mainly through **SETI@HOME,** the largest distributed computing project on Earth. Some of the world's largest radio telescopes, like the one built into a 20-acre natural bowl in Aricebo, Puerto Rico (pictured above), collect data from the most likely regions of our galaxy. The data are analyzed by personal computer users around the world. The four millionth participant registered on October 1, 2002. To learn more, or if you would like a chance at being the first to "contact" an extraterrestrial civilization, check out the website www.setiathome.ssl.berkeley.edu.

For Further Thought

The Birthday Problem

A classic problem (with a surprising result) involves the probability that a given group of people will include at least one pair of people with the same birthday (the same day of the year, not necessarily the same year). This problem can be analyzed using the probability of a complement formula (Section 2.2) and the multiplication rule of probability from this section. Suppose there are three people in the group. Then

P(at least one duplication of birthdays)

$= 1 - P$(no duplications)   Complement formula

$= 1 - P$(2nd is different than
             1st and 3rd is different
             than 1st and 2nd)

$= 1 - \dfrac{364}{365} \cdot \dfrac{363}{365}$ Multiplication rule

$\approx 1 - .992$

$= .008$

(To simplify the calculations, we have assumed 365 possible birth dates, ignoring February 29.)

By doing more calculations like the one above, we find that the smaller the group, the smaller the probability of a duplication; the larger the group, the larger the probability of a duplication. The table below shows the probability of at least one duplication for numbers of people through 50.

For Group Discussion or Individual Investigation

1. Based on the data shown in the table, what are the odds in favor of a duplication in a group of 30 people?
2. Estimate from the table the least number of people for which the probability of duplication is at least $\frac{1}{2}$.
3. How small a group is required for the probability of a duplication to be *exactly* 0?
4. How large a group is required for the probability of a duplication to be *exactly* 1?

Number of People	Probability of at Least One Duplication	Number of People	Probability of at Least One Duplication	Number of People	Probability of at Least One Duplication
2	.003	19	.379	36	.832
3	.008	20	.411	37	.849
4	.016	21	.444	38	.864
5	.027	22	.476	39	.878
6	.040	23	.507	40	.891
7	.056	24	.538	41	.903
8	.074	25	.569	42	.914
9	.095	26	.598	43	.924
10	.117	27	.627	44	.933
11	.141	28	.654	45	.941
12	.167	29	.681	46	.948
13	.194	30	.706	47	.955
14	.223	31	.730	48	.961
15	.253	32	.753	49	.966
16	.284	33	.775	50	.970
17	.315	34	.795		
18	.347	35	.814		

2.3 EXERCISES

For each experiment, determine whether the two given events are independent.

1. **Tossing Coins** A fair coin is tossed twice. The events are "head on the first" and "head on the second."

2. **Rolling Dice** A pair of dice are rolled. The events are "even on the first" and "odd on the second."

3. **Comparing Planets' Mean Distances from the Sun** Two planets are selected, without replacement, from the list in Table 7. The events are "first is closer than Jupiter" and "second is farther than Neptune."

4. **Comparing Mean Distances from the Sun** Two celestial bodies are selected, with replacement, from the list in Table 7. The events are "first is closer than Earth" and "second is farther than Uranus."

5. **Guessing Answers on a Multiple-choice Test** The answers are all guessed on a twenty-question multiple-choice test. The events are "first answer is correct" and "last answer is correct."

6. **Selecting Committees of U.S. Senators** A committee of five is randomly selected from the 100 U.S. Senators. The events are "first member selected is a Republican" and "second member selected is a Republican." (Assume that there are both Republicans and non-Republicans in the Senate.)

Comparing Gender and Career Motivation of University Students *One hundred college seniors attending a career fair at a major northeastern university were categorized according to gender and according to primary career motivation, as summarized here.*

		Primary Career Motivation			
		Money	**Allowed to be Creative**	**Sense of Giving to Society**	**Total**
Gender	**Male**	18	21	19	58
	Female	14	13	15	42
	Total	32	34	34	100

If one of these students is to be selected at random, find the probability that the student selected will satisfy each condition.

7. female

8. motivated primarily by creativity

9. not motivated primarily by money

10. male and motivated primarily by money

11. male, given that primary motivation is a sense of giving to society

12. motivated primarily by money or creativity, given that the student is female

Selecting Pets *A pet store has seven puppies, including four poodles, two terriers, and one retriever. If Rebecka and Aaron, in that order, each select one puppy at random, with replacement (they may both select the same one), find the probability of each event.*

13. both select a poodle

14. Rebecka selects a retriever, Aaron selects a terrier

15. Rebecka selects a terrier, Aaron selects a retriever

16. both select a retriever

Selecting Pets *Suppose two puppies are selected as earlier, but this time without replacement (Rebecka and Aaron cannot both select the same puppy). Find the probability of each event.*

17. both select a poodle

18. Aaron selects a terrier, given Rebecka selects a poodle

19. Aaron selects a retriever, given Rebecka selects a poodle

20. Rebecka selects a retriever

21. Aaron selects a retriever, given Rebecka selects a retriever

22. both select a retriever

Drawing Cards *Let two cards be dealt successively,* without replacement, *from a standard 52-card deck. Find the probability of each event in Exercises 23–27.*

23. spade second, given spade first

24. club second, given diamond first

25. two face cards

26. no face cards

27. The first card is a jack and the second is a face card.

28. Given events A and B within the sample space S, the following sequence of steps establishes formulas that can be used to compute conditional probabilities. Justify each statement.

   (a) $P(A \text{ and } B) = P(A) \cdot P(B \mid A)$

   (b) Therefore, $P(B \mid A) = \dfrac{P(A \text{ and } B)}{P(A)}$.

   (c) Therefore, $P(B \mid A) = \dfrac{n(A \text{ and } B)/n(S)}{n(A)/n(S)}$.

   (d) Therefore, $P(B \mid A) = \dfrac{n(A \text{ and } B)}{n(A)}$.

Considering Conditions in Card Drawing *Use the results of Exercise 28 to find each probability when a single card is drawn from a standard 52-card deck.*

29. $P(\text{queen} \mid \text{face card})$ **30.** $P(\text{face card} \mid \text{queen})$

31. $P(\text{red} \mid \text{diamond})$ **32.** $P(\text{diamond} \mid \text{red})$

33. If one number is chosen randomly from the integers 1 through 10, the probability of getting a number that is *odd and prime,* by the multiplication rule, is

$$P(\text{odd}) \cdot P(\text{prime} \mid \text{odd}) = \frac{5}{10} \cdot \frac{3}{5} = \frac{3}{10}.$$

Compute the product $P(\text{prime}) \cdot P(\text{odd} \mid \text{prime})$, and compare to the product above.

34. What does Exercise 33 imply, in general, about the probability of an event of the form A and B?

35. Gender in Sequences of Babies One of the authors of this book has three sons and no daughters. Assuming boy and girl babies are equally likely, what is the probability of this event?

36. Gender in Sequences of Babies Under the assumptions of Exercise 35, what is the probability that three successive births will be a boy, then a girl, then a boy?

The remaining exercises, and groups of exercises, may require concepts from earlier sections, such as the complements principle of counting and addition rules, as well as the multiplication rule of this section.

Probabilities in Warehouse Grocery Shopping *Emily Falzon manages a grocery warehouse which encourages volume shopping on the part of its customers. Emily has discovered that, on any given weekday, 80 percent of the customer sales amount to more than $100. That is, any given sale on such a day has a probability of .80 of being for more than $100. (Actually, the conditional probabilities throughout the day would change slightly, depending on earlier sales, but this effect would be negligible for the first several sales of the day, so we can treat them as independent.)*

Find the probability of each event. (Give answers to three decimal places.)

37. The first two sales on Wednesday are both for more than $100.

38. The first three sales on Wednesday are all for more than $100.

39. None of the first three sales on Wednesday is for more than $100.

40. Exactly one of the first three sales on Wednesday is for more than $100.

Pollution from the Space Shuttle Launch Site *One problem encountered by developers of the space shuttle program is air pollution in the area surrounding the launch site. A certain direction from the launch site is considered critical in terms of hydrogen chloride pollution from the exhaust cloud. It has been determined that weather conditions would cause emission cloud movement in the critical direction only 5% of the time.*

In Exercises 41–44 on the next page, find the probability for each event. Assume that probabilities for a particular launch in no way depend on the probabilities for other launches. (Give answers to two decimal places.)

41. A given launch will not result in cloud movement in the critical direction.

42. No cloud movement in the critical direction will occur during any of 5 launches.

43. Any 5 launches will result in at least one cloud movement in the critical direction.

44. Any 10 launches will result in at least one cloud movement in the critical direction.

Ordering Job Interviews *Four men and three women are waiting to be interviewed for jobs. If they are all selected in random order, find the probability of each event in Exercises 45–49.*

45. All the women will be interviewed first.

46. All the men will be interviewed first.

47. The first person interviewed will be a woman.

48. The second person interviewed will be a woman.

49. The last person interviewed will be a woman.

50. In Example 8, where Anne draws three balls without replacement, what would be her probability of getting one of each color, where the order does not matter?

51. ***Gender in Sequences of Babies*** Assuming boy and girl babies are equally likely, find the probability that it would take
   (a) at least three births to obtain two girls,
   (b) at least four births to obtain two girls,
   (c) at least five births to obtain two girls.

52. ***Drawing Cards*** Cards are drawn, without replacement, from an ordinary 52-card deck.
   (a) How many must be drawn before the probability of obtaining at least one face card is greater than $\frac{1}{2}$?
   (b) How many must be drawn before the probability of obtaining at least one king is greater than $\frac{1}{2}$?

Fair Decisions from Biased Coins *Many everyday decisions, like who will drive to lunch, or who will pay for the coffee, are made by the toss of a (presumably fair) coin and using the criterion "heads, you will; tails, I will." This criterion is not quite fair, however, if the coin is biased (perhaps due to slightly irregular construction or wear). John von Neumann suggested a way to make perfectly fair decisions even with a possibly biased coin. If a coin, biased so that*

$$P(h) = .5200 \quad \text{and} \quad P(t) = .4800,$$

is tossed twice, find each probability. (Give answers to four decimal places.)

53. $P(\text{hh})$ **54.** $P(\text{ht})$

55. $P(\text{th})$ **56.** $P(\text{tt})$

57. Having completed Exercises 53–56, can you suggest what von Neumann's scheme may have been?

Programming a Garage Door Opener *A certain brand of automatic garage door opener utilizes a transmitter control with six independent switches, each one set on or off. The receiver (wired to the door) must be set with the same pattern as the transmitter.* *Exercises 58–61 are based on ideas similar to those of the "birthday problem" in the "For Further Thought" feature in this section.*

58. How many different ways can the owner of one of these garage door openers set the switches?

59. If two residents in the same neighborhood each have one of this brand of opener, and both set the switches randomly, what is the probability to four decimal places that they are able to open each other's garage doors?

60. If five neighbors with the same type of opener set their switches independently, what is the probability of at least one pair of neighbors using the same settings? (Give your answer to four decimal places.)

61. What is the minimum number of neighbors who must use this brand of opener before the probability of at least one duplication of settings is greater than $\frac{1}{2}$?

62. ***Choosing Cards*** There are three cards, one that is green on both sides, one that is red on both sides, and one that is green on one side and red on the other. One of the three cards is selected randomly and laid on the table. If it happens that the card on the table has a red side up, what is the probability that it is also red on the other side?

---

*For more information, see "Matching Garage-Door Openers," by Bonnie H. Litwiller and David R. Duncan in the March 1992 issue of *Mathematics Teacher*, p. 217.

Weather Conditions on Successive Days *In November, the rain in a certain valley tends to fall in storms of several days' duration. The unconditional probability of rain on any given day of the month is .500. But the probability of rain on a day that follows a rainy day is .800, and the probability of rain on a day following a nonrainy day is .300. Find the probability of each event. Give answers to three decimal places.*

63. rain on two randomly selected consecutive days in November

64. rain on three randomly selected consecutive days in November

65. rain on November 1 and 2, but not on November 3

66. rain on the first four days of November, given that October 31 was clear all day

Engine Failures in a Vintage Aircraft *In a certain four-engine vintage aircraft, now quite unreliable, each engine has a 10% chance of failure on any flight, as long as it is carrying its one-fourth share of the load. But if one engine fails, then the chance of failure increases to 20% for each of the other three engines. And if a second engine fails, each of the remaining two has a 30% chance of failure. Assuming that no two engines ever fail simultaneously, and that the aircraft can continue flying with as few as two operating engines, find each probability for a given flight of this aircraft. (Give answers to four decimal places.)*

67. no engine failures

68. exactly one engine failure (any one of four engines)

69. exactly two engine failures (any two of four engines)

70. a failed flight

One-and-one Foul Shooting in Basketball *In basketball, "one-and-one" foul shooting is done as follows: if the player makes the first shot (1 point), he is given a second shot. If he misses the first shot, he is not given a second shot (see the tree diagram).*

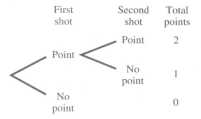

Susan Dratch, a basketball player, has a 70% foul shot record. (She makes 70% of her foul shots.) Find the probability that, on a given one-and-one foul shooting opportunity, Susan will score each number of points.

71. no points   **72.** one point

73. two points

74. **Comparing Empirical and Theoretical Probabilities in Dice Rolling** Roll a pair of dice until a sum of seven appears, keeping track of how many rolls it took. Repeat the process a total of 50 times, each time recording the number of rolls it took to get a sum of seven.

(a) Use your experimental data to compute an empirical probability (to two decimal places) that it would take at least three rolls to get a sum of seven.

(b) Find the theoretical probability (to two decimal places) that it would take at least three rolls to obtain a sum of seven.

75. Go to the Web site mentioned in the *natural disasters* margin note in this section and write a report on the threat to humanity of cosmic impacts. Include an explanation of the abbreviation *NEO*.

2.4 Binomial Probability

Binomial Probability Distribution • Binomial Probability Formula

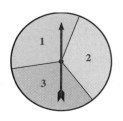

Binomial Probability Distribution   Suppose the spinner in the margin is spun twice, where we are interested in the number of times a 2 is obtained. (Assume each of the three sectors contains a 120-degree arc, so that each sector is equally likely on a given spin.) We can think of the outcome 2 as a "success," while outcomes 1 and 3 would be "failures." When the outcomes of an experiment are divided into just two categories, success and failure, the associated probabilities are called "binomial" (the prefix *bi* meaning *two*). Repeated performances of such an experiment, where the probability of success remains constant throughout all repetitions, are also known as repeated **Bernoulli trials** (after James Bernoulli). If we use an ordered pair to represent the result of each pair of spins, then the sample space for this experiment is

$$S = \{(1, 1), (1, 2), (1, 3), (2, 1), (2, 2), (2, 3), (3, 1), (3, 2), (3, 3)\}.$$

The nine outcomes in S are all equally likely. (This follows from the numbers 1, 2, and 3 being equally likely on a particular spin.)

If x denotes the number of 2s occurring on each pair of spins, then x is an example of a *random variable*. Although we cannot predict the result of any particular pair of spins, we can compute likelihoods, or probabilities, of various events from the sample space listing. In S, the number of 2s is 0 in four cases, 1 in four cases, and 2 in one case, as reflected in Table 8. Because the table includes all possible values of x, together with their probabilities, it is an example of a *probability distribution*. In this case, we have a **binomial probability distribution.** Notice that the probability column in Table 8 has a sum of 1, in agreement with property 3 of probability (Section 2.2).

In order to develop a general formula for binomial probabilities, we can consider another way to obtain the probability values in Table 8. The various spins of the spinner are independent of one another, and on each spin the probability of success (S) is $\frac{1}{3}$ and the probability of failure (F) is $\frac{2}{3}$. We will denote success on the first spin by S_1, failure on the second by F_2, and so on. Then, using the rules of probability, we have

$$
\begin{aligned}
P(x = 0) &= P(F_1 \text{ and } F_2) \\
&= P(F_1) \cdot P(F_2) \quad &\text{Multiplication rule} \\
&= \frac{2}{3} \cdot \frac{2}{3} \quad &\text{Substitute values.} \\
&= \frac{4}{9},
\end{aligned}
$$

$$
\begin{aligned}
P(x = 1) &= P[(S_1 \text{ and } F_2) \text{ or } (F_1 \text{ and } S_2)] \quad &\text{2 ways to get } x = 1 \\
&= P(S_1 \text{ and } F_2) + P(F_1 \text{ and } S_2) \quad &\text{Addition rule} \\
&= P(S_1) \cdot P(F_2) + P(F_1) \cdot P(S_2) \quad &\text{Multiplication rule} \\
&= \frac{1}{3} \cdot \frac{2}{3} + \frac{2}{3} \cdot \frac{1}{3} \quad &\text{Substitute values.} \\
&= \frac{2}{9} + \frac{2}{9} \\
&= \frac{4}{9},
\end{aligned}
$$

and
$$
\begin{aligned}
P(x = 2) &= P(S_1 \text{ and } S_2) \\
&= P(S_1) \cdot P(S_2) \quad &\text{Multiplication rule} \\
&= \frac{1}{3} \cdot \frac{1}{3} \quad &\text{Substitute values.} \\
&= \frac{1}{9}.
\end{aligned}
$$

James Bernoulli (1654–1705) is also known as Jacob or Jacques. He was charmed away from theology by the writings of Leibniz, became his pupil, and later headed the mathematics faculty at the University of Basel. His results in probability are contained in the *Art of Conjecture*, which was published in 1713, after his death, and which also included a reprint of the earlier Huygens paper. Bernoulli also made many contributions to calculus and analytic geometry.

Notice the following pattern in the above calculations. There is only one way to get $x = 0$ (namely, F_1 and F_2). And there is only one way to get $x = 2$ (namely, S_1 and S_2). But there are two ways to get $x = 1$. One way is S_1 and F_2; the other is F_1 and S_2. There are two ways because the one success required can occur on the first spin or on the second spin. How many ways can exactly one success occur in two repeated trials? This question is equivalent to:

How many size-one subsets are there of the set of two trials?

The answer is $_2C_1 = 2$. (The expression $_2C_1$ denotes "combinations of 2 things taken 1 at a time." Combinations were discussed in Section 1.3.) Each of the two ways to get exactly one success has a probability equal to $\frac{1}{3} \cdot \frac{2}{3}$, the probability of success times the probability of failure.

If the same spinner is spun three times rather than two, then x, the number of successes (2s) could have values of 0, 1, 2, or 3. Then the number of ways to get exactly 1 success is $_3C_1 = 3$. They are: S_1 and F_2 and F_3, F_1 and S_2 and F_3, F_1 and F_2 and S_3. The probability of each of these three ways is $\frac{1}{3} \cdot \frac{2}{3} \cdot \frac{2}{3} = \frac{4}{27}$. So

$$P(x = 1) = 3 \cdot \frac{4}{27} = \frac{12}{27} = \frac{4}{9}.$$

Figure 11 shows all possibilities for three spins, and Table 9 gives the associated probability distribution. In the tree diagram, the number of ways of getting two successes in three trials is 3, in agreement with the fact that $_3C_2 = 3$. Also the sum of the $P(x)$ column in Table 9 is again 1.

TABLE 9

Probability Distribution for the Number of 2s in Three Spins

x	$P(x)$
0	$\frac{8}{27}$
1	$\frac{12}{27}$
2	$\frac{6}{27}$
3	$\frac{1}{27}$
	Sum $= \frac{27}{27} = 1$

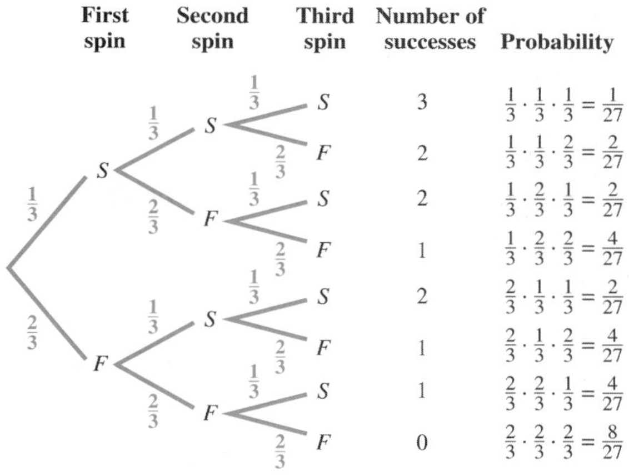

Tree diagram for three spins

FIGURE 11

PROBLEM-SOLVING HINT   One of the problem-solving strategies was "Look for a pattern." Having constructed complete probability distributions for binomial experiments with 2 and 3 repeated trials (and probability of success $\frac{1}{3}$), we can now generalize the observed pattern to any binomial experiment, as shown next.

Binomial Probability Formula   In general, let

n = the number of repeated trials,

p = the probability of success on any given trial,

$q = 1 - p$ = the probability of failure on any given trial,

and x = the number of successes that occur.

Note that p remains fixed throughout all n trials. This means that all trials are independent of one another. The random variable x (number of successes) can have any integer value from 0 through n. In general, x successes can be assigned among n repeated trials in ${}_nC_x$ different ways, since this is the number of different subsets of x positions among a set of n positions. Also, regardless of which x of the trials result in successes, there will always be x successes and $n - x$ failures, so we multiply x factors of p and $n - x$ factors of q together.

Binomial Probability Formula

When n independent repeated trials occur, where

$$p = \text{probability of success} \quad \text{and} \quad q = \text{probability of failure}$$

with p and q (where $q = 1 - p$) remaining constant throughout all n trials, the probability of exactly x successes is given by

$$P(x) = {}_nC_x\, p^x q^{n-x} = \frac{n!}{x!(n - x)!}\, p^x q^{n-x}.$$

From the
DISTR menu

```
binompdf(5,.5,3)
              .3125
Ans▸Frac
              5/16
```

The TI-83/84 Plus calculator will find the probability discussed in Example 1.

Tables of binomial probability values are commonly available in statistics texts, for various values of p, often for n ranging up to about 20. Also, computer software packages for statistics will usually do these calculations for you automatically, as will some handheld calculators. In the following examples, we use the formula.

EXAMPLE 1   Finding Probability in Coin Tossing

Find the probability of obtaining exactly three heads in five tosses of a fair coin.

SOLUTION

Let heads be "success." Then this is a binomial experiment with $n = 5$, $p = \frac{1}{2}$, $q = \frac{1}{2}$, and $x = 3$. By the binomial probability formula,

$$P(3) = {}_5C_3\left(\frac{1}{2}\right)^3\left(\frac{1}{2}\right)^2 = 10 \cdot \frac{1}{8} \cdot \frac{1}{4} = \frac{5}{16}.$$ ∎

```
binompdf(6,1/6,2
)
           .200938786
```

This screen supports the answer in Example 2.

EXAMPLE 2   Finding Probability in Dice Rolling

Find the probability of obtaining exactly two 5s in six rolls of a fair die.

SOLUTION

Let 5 be "success." Then $n = 6$, $p = \frac{1}{6}$, $q = \frac{5}{6}$, and $x = 2$.

$$P(2) = {}_6C_2\left(\frac{1}{6}\right)^2\left(\frac{5}{6}\right)^4 = 15 \cdot \frac{1}{36} \cdot \frac{625}{1296} = \frac{3125}{15,552} \approx .201$$ ∎

In the case of repeated independent trials, when an event involves more than one specific number of successes, we can employ the binomial probability formula along with the complement or addition rules.

```
binompdf(5,.5,4)
+binompdf(5,.5,5
)
            .1875
Ans▶Frac
              3/16
```

This screen supports the answer in Example 3.

EXAMPLE 3 Finding Probability of Female Children

A couple plans to have 5 children. Find the probability they will have more than 3 girls. (Assume girl and boy babies are equally likely.)

SOLUTION

Let a girl be "success." Then $n = 5$, $p = q = \frac{1}{2}$, and $x > 3$.

$$P(x > 3) = P(x = 4 \text{ or } 5) \qquad \text{More than 3 means 4 or 5.}$$

$$= P(4) + P(5) \qquad \text{Addition rule}$$

$$= {}_5C_4\left(\frac{1}{2}\right)^4\left(\frac{1}{2}\right)^1 + {}_5C_5\left(\frac{1}{2}\right)^5\left(\frac{1}{2}\right)^0 \qquad \text{Binomial probability formula}$$

$$= 5 \cdot \frac{1}{16} \cdot \frac{1}{2} + 1 \cdot \frac{1}{32} \cdot 1 \qquad \text{Simplify.}$$

$$= \frac{5}{32} + \frac{1}{32} = \frac{6}{32} = \frac{3}{16} = .1875$$

```
1-(binompdf(10,.
3,0)+binompdf(10
,.3,1)+binompdf(
10,.3,2))
       .6172172136
```

This screen supports the answer in Example 4.

EXAMPLE 4 Finding Probability of Hits in Baseball

Scott Davidson, a baseball player, has a well-established career batting average of .300. In a brief series with a rival team, Scott will bat 10 times. Find the probability that he will get more than two hits in the series.

SOLUTION

This "experiment" involves $n = 10$ repeated Bernoulli trials, with probability of success (a hit) given by $p = .3$ (which implies $q = 1 - .3 = .7$). Since, in this case, "more than 2" means

"3 or 4 or 5 or 6 or 7 or 8 or 9 or 10"

(which is eight different possibilities), it will be less work to apply the complement rule.

$$P(x > 2) = 1 - P(x \le 2) \qquad \text{Complement rule}$$

$$= 1 - P(x = 0 \text{ or } 1 \text{ or } 2) \qquad \text{Only three different possibilities}$$

$$= 1 - [P(0) + P(1) + P(2)] \qquad \text{Addition rule}$$

$$= 1 - [{}_{10}C_0(.3)^0(.7)^{10} \qquad \text{Binomial probability formula}$$

$$\quad + {}_{10}C_1(.3)^1(.7)^9 + {}_{10}C_2(.3)^2(.7)^8]$$

$$\approx 1 - [.0282 + .1211 + .2335] \qquad \text{Simplify.}$$

$$= 1 - .3828$$

$$= .6172$$

For Further Thought

First Success on Trial x

In the case of n independent repeated Bernoulli trials, the formula developed in this section gives the probability of exactly x successes. Sometimes, however, we are interested not in the event that exactly x successes will occur in n trials, but rather the event that the first success will occur on the xth trial. Consider the probability that, in a series of coin tosses, the first success (head) will occur on the fourth toss. This implies a failure first, then a second failure, then a third failure, and finally a success. Symbolically, the event is F_1 and F_2 and F_3 and S_4. The probability of this sequence of outcomes is $q \cdot q \cdot q \cdot p$, or $q^3 \cdot p$. In general, if the probability of success stays constant at p (which implies a probability of failure of $q = 1 - p$), then the probability that the first success will occur on the xth trial can be computed as follows.

$$P(F_1 \text{ and } F_2 \ldots \text{ and } F_{x-1} \text{ and } S_x) = q^{x-1} \cdot p$$

For Group Discussion or Individual Investigation

1. Explain why, in the formula above, there is no combination factor, such as the $_nC_x$ in the binomial probability formula.
2. **Union Members in an Industry** If 30 percent of all workers in a certain industry are union members, and workers in this industry are selected successively at random, find the probability that the first union member to occur will be on the third selection.
3. **Getting Caught when Speeding** If the probability of getting caught when you exceed the speed limit on a certain stretch of highway is .38, find the probability that the first time you will get caught is the fourth time that you exceed the speed limit.
4. **Gender in Sequences of Babies** Assuming male and female babies are equally likely, find the probability that a family's fourth child will be their first daughter.

5. **Aborted Rocket Launches** If a certain type of rocket always has a four percent chance of an aborted launching, find the probability that the first launch to be aborted is the 20th launch.

2.4 EXERCISES

For Exercises 1–24, give all numerical answers as common fractions reduced to lowest terms. For Exercises 25–54, give all numerical answers to three decimal places.

Coin Tossing *If three fair coins are tossed, find the probability of each number of heads.*

1. 0	**2.** 1	**3.** 2
4. 3	**5.** 1 or 2	**6.** at least 1
7. no more than 1	**8.** fewer than 3	

9. **Gender in Sequences of Babies** Assuming boy and girl babies are equally likely, find the probability that a family with three children will have exactly two boys.

10. Pascal's triangle was shown in Table 5 of Section 1.4. Explain how the probabilities in Exercises 1–4 here relate to row 3 of the "triangle." (Recall that we referred to the topmost row of the triangle as "row number 0," and to the leftmost entry of each row as "entry number 0.")

11. Generalize the pattern in Exercise 10 to complete the following statement. If *n* fair coins are tossed, the probability of exactly *x* heads is the fraction whose numerator is entry number ___ of row number ___ in Pascal's triangle, and whose denominator is the sum of the entries in row number ___.

Binomial Probability Applied to Tossing Coins Use the pattern noted in Exercises 10 and 11 to find the probabilities of each number of heads when seven fair coins are tossed.

12. 0   **13.** 1   **14.** 2   **15.** 3

16. 4   **17.** 5   **18.** 6   **19.** 7

Binomial Probability Applied to Rolling Dice A fair die is rolled three times. A 4 is considered "success," while all other outcomes are "failures." Find the probability of each number of successes.

20. 0   **21.** 1

22. 2   **23.** 3

24. Exercises 10 and 11 established a way of using Pascal's triangle rather than the binomial probability formula to find probabilities of different numbers of successes in coin-tossing experiments. Explain why the same process would not work for Exercises 20–23.

For n repeated independent trials, with constant probability of success p for all trials, find the probability of exactly x successes in each case.

25. $n = 5$, $p = \frac{1}{3}$, $x = 4$

26. $n = 10$, $p = .7$, $x = 5$

27. $n = 20$, $p = \frac{1}{8}$, $x = 2$

28. $n = 30$, $p = .6$, $x = 22$

For Exercises 29–31, refer to Example 4.

29. *Batting Averages in Baseball* Does Scott's probability of a hit really remain constant at exactly .300 through all ten times at bat? Explain your reasoning.

30. *Batting Averages in Baseball* If Scott's batting average is exactly .300 going into the series, and that value is based on exactly 1200 career hits out of 4000 previous times at bat, what is the greatest his average could possibly be (to three decimal places) when he goes up to bat the tenth time of the series? What is the least his average could possibly be when he goes up to bat the tenth time of the series?

31. Do you think the use of the binomial probability formula was justified in Example 4, even though *p* is not strictly constant? Explain your reasoning.

Random Selection of Answers on a Multiple-choice Test Yesha Brill is taking a ten-question multiple-choice test for which each question has three answer choices, only one of which is correct. Yesha decides on answers by rolling a fair die and marking the first answer choice if the die shows 1 or 2, the second if it shows 3 or 4, and the third if it shows 5 or 6. Find the probability of each event.

32. exactly four correct answers

33. exactly seven correct answers

34. fewer than three correct answers

35. at least seven correct answers

Side Effects of Prescription Drugs It is known that a certain prescription drug produces undesirable side effects in 30% of all patients who use it. Among a random sample of eight patients using the drug, find the probability of each event.

36. None have undesirable side effects.

37. Exactly one has undesirable side effects.

38. Exactly two have undesirable side effects.

39. More than two have undesirable side effects.

Likelihood of Capable Students Attending College In a certain state, it has been shown that only 50% of the high school graduates who are capable of college work actually enroll in colleges. Find the probability that, among nine capable high school graduates in this state, each number will enroll in college.

40. exactly 4   **41.** from 4 through 6

42. none   **43.** all 9

44. *Student Ownership of Personal Computers* At a large midwestern university, 80% of all students have their own personal computers. If five students at that university are selected at random, find the probability that exactly three of them have their own computers.

45. *Frost Survival Among Orange Trees* If it is known that 65% of all orange trees will survive a hard frost, then what is the probability that at least half of a group of six trees will survive such a frost?

46. *Rate of Favorable Media Coverage of an Incumbent President* An extensive survey revealed that, during a certain presidential election campaign, 64% of the political columns in a certain group of major newspapers were favorable to the incumbent president. If a sample of fifteen of these columns is selected at random, what is the probability that exactly ten of them will be favorable?

Samantha stands on the street corner tossing a coin. She decides she will toss it 10 times, each time walking 1 block north if it lands heads up, and 1 block south if it lands tails up. In each of the following exercises, find the probability that she will end up in the indicated location. (In each case, ask how many successes, say heads, would be required and use the binomial formula. Some ending positions may not be possible with 10 tosses.) The random process involved here illustrates what we call a **random walk.** It is a simplified model of Brownian motion, mentioned on page 56. Further applications of the idea of a random walk are found in the Extension at the end of this chapter.

47. 10 blocks north of her corner

48. 6 blocks north of her corner

49. 6 blocks south of her corner

50. 5 blocks south of her corner

51. 2 blocks north of her corner

52. at least 2 blocks north of her corner

53. at least 2 blocks from her corner

54. on her corner

2.5 **Expected Value**

Expected Value • Games and Gambling • Investments • Business and Insurance

TABLE 10	
x	$P(x)$
1	.05
2	.10
3	.20
4	.40
5	.10
6	.15

Expected Value The probability distribution in Table 10, from Example 6 of Section 2.2, shows the probabilities assigned by Jacob to the various lengths of time his homework may take on a given night. If Jacob's friend Omer asks him how many hours his studies will take, what would be his best guess? Six different time values are possible, with some more likely than others. One thing Jacob could do is calculate a "weighted average" by multiplying each possible time value by its probability and then adding the six products.

$$1(.05) + 2(.10) + 3(.20) + 4(.40) + 5(.10) + 6(.15)$$
$$= .05 + .20 + .60 + 1.60 + .50 + .90 = 3.85$$

Thus 3.85 hours is the **expected value** (or the **mathematical expectation**) of the quantity of time to be spent. Since the original time values in the table were rounded to the nearest hour, the expected value also should be rounded, to 4 hours.

> **Expected Value**
>
> If a random variable x can have any of the values $x_1, x_2, x_3, \ldots, x_n$, and the corresponding probabilities of these values occurring are $P(x_1), P(x_2), P(x_3), \ldots, P(x_n)$, then the **expected value of x** is given by
>
> $$E(x) = x_1 \cdot P(x_1) + x_2 \cdot P(x_2) + x_3 \cdot P(x_3) + \cdots + x_n \cdot P(x_n).$$

Solution to the Chapter Opener Problem One way to look at the problem, given that the car is *not* behind Door 3, is that Doors 1 and 2 are now equally likely to contain the car. Thus, switching doors will neither help nor hurt your chances of winning the car.

However, there is another way to look at the problem. When you picked Door 1, the probability was $\frac{1}{3}$ that it contained the car. Being shown the goat behind Door 3 doesn't really give you any new information; after all, you knew that there was a goat behind at least one of the other doors. So seeing the goat behind Door 3 does nothing to change your assessment of the probability that Door 1 has the car. It remains $\frac{1}{3}$. But because Door 3 has been ruled out, the probability that Door 2 has the car is now $\frac{2}{3}$. Thus, you should switch.

Analysis of this problem depends on the psychology of the host. If we suppose that the host must *always* show you a losing door and then give you an option to switch, then you should switch. This was not specifically stated in the problem as posed above but was pointed out by many mathematicians who became involved in the discussion.

(The authors wish to thank David Berman of the University of New Orleans for his assistance with this explanation.)

EXAMPLE 1 Finding the Expected Number of Boys

Find the expected number of boys for a three-child family (that is, the expected value of the number of boys). Assume girls and boys are equally likely.

SOLUTION

The sample space for this experiment is

$$S = \{\text{ggg, ggb, gbg, bgg, gbb, bgb, bbg, bbb}\}.$$

The probability distribution is shown in Table 11, along with the products and their sum, which gives the expected value.

TABLE 11

Number of Boys x	Probability $P(x)$	Product $x \cdot P(x)$
0	$\frac{1}{8}$	0
1	$\frac{3}{8}$	$\frac{3}{8}$
2	$\frac{3}{8}$	$\frac{6}{8}$
3	$\frac{1}{8}$	$\frac{3}{8}$

Expected value: $E(x) = \frac{12}{8} = \frac{3}{2}$

The expected number of boys is $\frac{3}{2}$, or 1.5. This result seems reasonable. Since boys and girls are equally likely, "half" the children are expected to be boys.

Notice that the expected value for the number of boys in the family is itself an impossible value. So, the expected value itself could never occur. Many times the expected value actually cannot occur; it is only a kind of long run average of the various values that could occur. If we recorded the number of boys in many different three-child families, then by the law of large numbers, as the number of observed families increased, the observed average number of boys should approach the expected value.

Example 1 did not involve money, but many uses of expected value do involve monetary expectations. Common applications are in gambling, investments, and business decisions.

Games and Gambling

EXAMPLE 2 Finding Expected Winnings

A player pays $3 to play the following game: He tosses three fair coins and receives back "payoffs" of $1 if he tosses no heads, $2 for one head, $3 for two heads, and $4 for three heads. Find the player's expected net winnings for this game.

SOLUTION

Display the information as in Table 12 on the next page. (Notice that, for each possible event, "net winnings" are "gross winnings" (payoff) minus cost to play.) Probabilities are derived from the sample space

$$S = \{\text{ttt, htt, tht, tth, hht, hth, thh, hhh}\}.$$

TABLE 12

Number of Heads	Payoff	Net Winnings x	Probability $P(x)$	Product $x \cdot P(x)$
0	$1	$-$2$	$\frac{1}{8}$	$-\$\frac{2}{8}$
1	2	-1	$\frac{3}{8}$	$-\frac{3}{8}$
2	3	0	$\frac{3}{8}$	0
3	4	1	$\frac{1}{8}$	$\frac{1}{8}$

Expected value: $E(x) = -\$\frac{1}{2} = -\$.50$

The expected net loss of 50 cents is a long-run average only. On any particular play of this game, the player would lose $2 or lose $1 or break even or win $1. Over a long series of plays, say 100, there would be some wins and some losses, but the total net result would likely be around a $100 \cdot (\$.50) = \$50$ *loss*. ■

A game in which the expected net winnings are zero is called a **fair game.** The game in Example 2 has negative expected net winnings, so it is unfair against the player. A game with positive expected net winnings is unfair in favor of the player.

EXAMPLE 3   Finding the Cost for a Fair Game

The $3 cost to play the game of Example 2 makes the game unfair against the player (since the player's expected net winnings are negative). What cost would make this a fair game?

SOLUTION

We already computed, in Example 2, that the $3 cost to play resulted in an expected net loss of $.50. Therefore we can conclude that the $3 cost was 50 cents too high. A fair cost to play the game would then be $3 − $.50 = $2.50. ■

The result in Example 3 can be verified as follows. First disregard the cost to play and find the expected *gross* winnings (by summing the products of payoff times probability).

$$E(\text{gross winnings}) = \$1 \cdot \frac{1}{8} + \$2 \cdot \frac{3}{8} + \$3 \cdot \frac{3}{8} + \$4 \cdot \frac{1}{8} = \frac{\$20}{8} = \$2.50$$

Since the long-run expected gross winnings (payoff) are $2.50, this amount is a fair cost to play.

EXAMPLE 4   Finding the Cost for a Fair Game

In a certain state lottery, a player chooses three digits, in a specific order. (Leading digits may be 0, so numbers such as 028 and 003 are legitimate entries.) The lottery operators randomly select a three-digit sequence, and any player matching their selection receives a payoff of $600. What is a fair cost to play this game?

SOLUTION

In this case, no cost has been proposed, so we have no choice but to compute expected gross winnings. The probability of selecting all three digits correctly is $\frac{1}{10} \cdot \frac{1}{10} \cdot \frac{1}{10} = \frac{1}{1000}$, and the probability of not selecting all three correctly is $1 - \frac{1}{1000} = \frac{999}{1000}$. The expected gross winnings are

$$E(\text{gross winnings}) = \$600 \cdot \frac{1}{1000} + \$0 \cdot \frac{999}{1000} = \$.60.$$

Thus the fair cost to play this game is 60 cents. (In fact, the lottery charges $1 to play, so players should expect to lose 40 cents per play *on the average*.) ▪

Of course, state lotteries must be unfair against players because they are designed to help fund benefits (such as the state's school system) as well as to cover administrative costs and certain other expenses. Among people's reasons for playing may be a willingness to support such causes, but most people undoubtedly play for the chance to "beat the odds" and be one of the few net winners.

Gaming casinos are major business enterprises, by no means designed to break even; the games they offer are always unfair in favor of the house. The bias does not need to be great, however, since even relatively small average losses per player multiplied by large numbers of players can result in huge profits for the house.

Roulette ("little wheel") was invented in France in the seventeenth or early eighteenth century. It has been a featured game of chance in the gambling casino of Monte Carlo.

The disk is divided into red and black alternating compartments, numbered 1 to 36 (but not in that order). There is a compartment also for 0 (and for 00 in the United States). In roulette, the wheel is set in motion, and an ivory ball is thrown into the bowl opposite to the direction of the wheel. When the wheel stops, the ball comes to rest in one of the compartments—the number and color determine who wins.

The players bet against the banker (person in charge of the pool of money) by placing money or equivalent chips in spaces on the roulette table corresponding to the wheel's colors or numbers. Bets can be made on one number or several, on odd or even, on red or black, or on combinations. The banker pays off according to the odds against the particular bet(s). For example, the classic payoff for a winning single number is $36 for each $1 bet.

EXAMPLE 5 Finding Expected Winnings in Roulette

One simple type of *roulette* is played with an ivory ball and a wheel set in motion. The wheel contains thirty-eight compartments. Eighteen of the compartments are black, eighteen are red, one is labeled "zero," and one is labeled "double zero." (These last two are neither black nor red.) In this case, assume the player places $1 on either red or black. If the player picks the correct color of the compartment in which the ball finally lands, the payoff is $2; otherwise the payoff is zero. Find the expected net winnings.

SOLUTION

By the expected value formula, expected net winnings are

$$E(\text{net winnings}) = (\$1)\frac{18}{38} + (-\$1)\frac{20}{38} = -\$\frac{1}{19}.$$

The expected net loss here is $\$\frac{1}{19}$, or about 5.3¢, per play. ▪

Investments Expected value can be a useful tool for evaluating investment opportunities.

EXAMPLE 6 Finding Expected Investment Profits

Todd Hall has $5000 to invest and will commit the whole amount, for six months, to one of three technology stocks. A number of uncertainties could affect the prices of these stocks, but Todd is confident, based on his research, that one of only several possible profit scenarios will prove true of each one at the end of the six-month period.

His complete analysis is shown in Table 13. (For example, stock *ABC* could lose $400, gain $800, or gain $1500.)

TABLE 13

Company *ABC*		Company *RST*		Company *XYZ*	
Profit or Loss x	**Probability** $P(x)$	**Profit or Loss** x	**Probability** $P(x)$	**Profit or Loss** x	**Probability** $P(x)$
−$400	.2	$500	.8	$0	.4
800	.5	1000	.2	700	.3
1500	.3			1200	.1
				2000	.2

Find the expected profit (or loss) for each of the three stocks and select Todd's optimum choice based on these calculations.

SOLUTION

Apply the expected value formula.

$$\text{ABC}: \quad -\$400 \cdot (.2) + \$800 \cdot (.5) + \$1500 \cdot (.3) = \$770$$

$$\text{RST}: \quad \$500 \cdot (.8) + \$1000 \cdot (.2) = \$600$$

$$\text{XYZ}: \quad \$0 \cdot (.4) + \$700 \cdot (.3) + \$1200 \cdot (.1) + \$2000 \cdot (.2) = \$730$$

The largest expected profit is $770. By this analysis, Todd should invest the money in stock *ABC*. ◼

Of course, by investing in stock *ABC*, Todd may in fact *lose* $400 over the six months. The "expected" return of $770 is only a long-run average over many identical situations. Since this particular investment situation may never occur again, you may argue that using expected values is not the best approach for Todd to use.

One possible alternative would be to adopt the view of an optimist, who might ignore the various probabilities and just hope for the best possibility associated with each choice and make a decision accordingly. Or, on the other hand, a pessimist may assume the worst case probably will occur, and make a decision in accordance with that view.

EXAMPLE 7 Choosing Stock Investments

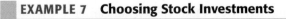

Decide which stock of Example 6 Todd would pick in each case.

(a) He is an optimist.   **(b)** He is a pessimist.

SOLUTION

(a) Disregarding the probabilities, he would focus on the best that could possibly happen with each stock. Since *ABC* could return as much as $1500, *RST* as much as $1000, and *XYZ* as much as $2000, the optimum is $2000. He would buy stock *XYZ*.

The first **Silver Dollar Slot Machine** was fashioned in 1929 by the Fey Manufacturing Company, San Francisco, inventors of the 3-reel, automatic payout machine (1895).

(b) In this case, he would focus on the worst possible cases. Since *ABC* might return as little as −$400 (a $400 loss), *RST* as little as $500, and *XYZ* as little as $0, he would buy stock *RST* (the best of the three worst cases). ▪

Business and Insurance   Expected value can be used to help make decisions in various areas of business, including insurance.

EXAMPLE 8   Finding Expected Lumber Revenue

Michael Crenshaw, a lumber wholesaler, is considering the purchase of a (railroad) carload of varied dimensional lumber. Michael calculates that the probabilities of reselling the load for $10,000, $9000, or $8000 are .22, .33, and .45, respectively. In order to ensure an *expected* profit of at least $3000, how much can Michael afford to pay for the load?

SOLUTION

The expected revenue (or income) from resales can be found in Table 14.

TABLE 14

Income x	Probability $P(x)$	Product $x \cdot P(x)$
$10,000	.22	$2200
9000	.33	2970
8000	.45	3600

Expected revenue: $8770

In general, we have the relationship

$$\text{profit} = \text{revenue} - \text{cost}.$$

Therefore, in terms of expectations,

$$\text{expected profit} = \text{expected revenue} - \text{cost}.$$

So $3000 = $8770 − cost,   or   equivalently,   cost = $8770 − $3000 = $5770. Michael can pay up to $5770 and still maintain an expected profit of at least $3000. ▪

EXAMPLE 9   Analyzing an Insurance Decision

A farmer will realize a profit of $150,000 on his wheat crop, unless there is rain before harvest, in which case he will realize only $40,000. The long-term weather forecast assigns rain a probability of .16. (So the probability of no rain is 1 − .16 = .84.) An insurance company offers crop insurance of $150,000 against rain for a premium of $20,000. Should the farmer buy the insurance?

SOLUTION

In order to make a wise decision, the farmer computes his expected profit under both options: to insure and not to insure. The complete calculations are summarized in the two "expectation" Tables 15 and 16.

For example, if insurance is purchased and it rains, the farmer's net profit is

$$\begin{bmatrix} \text{Insurance} \\ \text{proceeds} \end{bmatrix} + \begin{bmatrix} \text{Reduced} \\ \text{crop profit} \end{bmatrix} - \begin{bmatrix} \text{Insurance} \\ \text{premium} \end{bmatrix} \leftarrow \textit{Net profit}$$

$$\$150{,}000 \quad + \quad \$40{,}000 \quad - \quad \$20{,}000 \quad = \quad \$170{,}000.$$

TABLE 15

Expectation for Insuring

	Net Profit x	Probability $P(x)$	Product $x \cdot P(x)$
Rain	$170,000	.16	$27,200
No rain	130,000	.84	109,200

Expected profit: **$136,400**

TABLE 16

Expectation for Not Insuring

	Net Profit x	Probability $P(x)$	Product $x \cdot P(x)$
Rain	$40,000	.16	$6400
No rain	150,000	.84	126,000

Expected profit: **$132,400**

By comparing expected profits (**136,400 > 132,400**), we conclude that the farmer is better off buying the insurance. ■

For Further Thought

Expected Value of Games of Chance

Slot machines are a popular game for those who want to lose their money with very little mental effort. We cannot calculate an expected value applicable to all slot machines since payoffs vary from machine to machine. But we can calculate the "typical expected value."

A player operates a slot machine by pulling a handle after inserting a coin or coins. Reels inside

This Cleveland Indians fan hit four 7s in a row on a progressive nickel slot machine at the Sands Casino in Las Vegas in 1988.

(continued)

For Further Thought

the machine then rotate, and come to rest in some random order. Assume that three reels show the pictures listed in Table 17. For example, of the 20 pictures on the first reel, 2 are cherries, 5 are oranges, 5 are plums, 2 are bells, 2 are melons, 3 are bars, and 1 is the number 7.

A picture of cherries on the first reel, but not on the second, leads to a payoff of 3 coins (*net* winnings: 2 coins); a picture of cherries on the first two reels, but not the third, leads to a payoff of 5 coins (*net* winnings: 4 coins). All other winning combinations are as listed in Table 18.

Since, according to Table 17, there are 2 ways of getting cherries on the first reel, 15 ways of *not* getting cherries on the second reel, and 20 ways of getting anything on the third reel, we have a total of $2 \cdot 15 \cdot 20 = 600$ ways of getting a net payoff of 2. Since there are 20 pictures per reel, there are a total of $20 \cdot 20 \cdot 20 = 8000$ possible outcomes. Hence, the probability of receiving a net payoff of 2 coins is 600/8000. Table 18 takes into account all *winning* outcomes, with the necessary products for finding expectation added in the last column.

TABLE 17

Pictures	Reels		
	1	2	3
Cherries	2	5	4
Oranges	5	4	5
Plums	5	3	3
Bells	2	4	4
Melons	2	1	2
Bars	3	2	1
7s	1	1	1
Totals	20	20	20

TABLE 18 Calculating Expected Loss on a Three-Reel Slot Machine

Winning Combinations	Number of Ways	Probability	Number of Coins Received	Net Winnings (in coins)	Probability Times Winnings
1 cherry (on first reel)	$2 \cdot 15 \cdot 20 = 600$	600/8000	3	2	1200/8000
2 cherries (on first two reels)	$2 \cdot 5 \cdot 16 = 160$	160/8000	5	4	640/8000
3 cherries	$2 \cdot 5 \cdot 4 = 40$	40/8000	10	9	360/8000
3 oranges	$5 \cdot 4 \cdot 5 = 100$	100/8000	10	9	900/8000
3 plums	$5 \cdot 3 \cdot 3 = 45$	45/8000	14	13	585/8000
3 bells	$\_\_ \cdot \_\_ \cdot \_\_ = \_\_$	__/8000	18	___	____/8000
3 melons (jackpot)	$\_\_ \cdot \_\_ \cdot \_\_ = \_\_$	__/8000	100	___	____/8000
3 bars (jackpot)	$\_\_ \cdot \_\_ \cdot \_\_ = \_\_$	__/8000	200	___	____/8000
3 7s (jackpot)	$\_\_ \cdot \_\_ \cdot \_\_ = \_\_$	__/8000	500	___	____/8000
Totals	___				6318/8000

(continued)

For Further Thought

However, since a *nonwinning* outcome can occur in 8000 − 988 = 7012 ways (with winnings of − 1 coin), the product (− 1) · 7012/8000 must also be included. Hence, the expected value of this particular slot machine is

$$\frac{6318}{8000} + (-1) \cdot \frac{7012}{8000} \approx -.087 \text{ coin.}$$

On a machine costing one dollar per play, the expected *loss* (per play) is about

$$(.087) (1 \text{ dollar}) = 8.7 \text{ cents.}$$

Actual slot machines vary in expected loss per dollar of play. But author Hornsby was able to beat a Las Vegas slot machine in 1988. (See the photo on page 98.)

Table 19 comes from an article by Andrew Sterrett in *The Mathematics Teacher* (March 1967), in which he discusses rules for various games of chance and calculates their expected values. He uses expected values to find expected times it would take to lose $1000 if you played continually at the rate of $1 per play and one play per minute.

For Group Discussion or Individual Investigation

1. Explain why the entries of the "Net Winnings" column of Table 18 are all one fewer than the corresponding entries of the "Number of Coins Received" column.

2. Find the 29 missing values in Table 18. (Refer to Table 17 for the values in the "Number of Ways" column.)

3. In order to make your money last as long as possible in a casino, which game should you play?

TABLE 19 Expected Time to Lose $1000

Game	Expected Value	Days	Hours	Minutes
Roulette (with one 0)	−$.027	25	16	40
Roulette (with 0 and 00)	−$.053	13	4	40
Chuck-a-luck	−$.079	8	19	46
Keno (one number)	−$.200	3	11	20
Numbers	−$.300	2	7	33
Football pool (4 winners)	−$.375	1	20	27
Football pool (10 winners)	−$.658	1	1	19

2.5 EXERCISES

1. Explain in words what is meant by "expected value of a random variable."

2. Explain what a couple means by the statement, "We expect to have 1.5 sons."

3. **Tossing Coins** Five fair coins are tossed. Find the expected number of heads.

4. **Drawing Cards** Two cards are drawn, with replacement, from a standard 52-card deck. Find the expected number of diamonds.

Expected Winnings in a Die-rolling Game For Exercises 5 and 6, a game consists of rolling a single fair die and pays off as follows: $3 for a 6, $2 for a 5, $1 for a 4, and no payoff otherwise.

5. Find the expected winnings for this game.

6. What is a fair price to pay to play this game?

Expected Winnings in a Die-rolling Game *For Exercises 7 and 8, consider a game consisting of rolling a single fair die, with payoffs as follows. If an even number of spots turns up, you receive that many dollars. But if an odd number of spots turns up, you must pay that many dollars.*

7. Find the expected net winnings of this game.

8. Is this game fair, or unfair against the player, or unfair in favor of the player?

9. ***Expected Winnings in a Coin-tossing Game*** A certain game involves tossing 3 fair coins, and it pays 10¢ for 3 heads, 5¢ for 2 heads, and 3¢ for 1 head. Is 5¢ a fair price to pay to play this game? (That is, does the 5¢ cost to play make the game fair?)

10. ***Expected Winnings in Roulette*** In a form of roulette slightly different from that in Example 5, a more generous management supplies a wheel having only thirty-seven compartments, with eighteen red, eighteen black, and one zero. Find the expected net winnings if you bet on red in this game.

11. ***Expected Number of Absences in a Math Class*** In a certain mathematics class, the probabilities have been empirically determined for various numbers of absences on any given day. These values are shown in the table below. Find the expected number of absences on a given day. (Give the answer to two decimal places.)

Number absent	0	1	2	3	4
Probability	.12	.32	.35	.14	.07

12. ***Expected Profit of an Insurance Company*** An insurance company will insure a $100,000 home for its total value for an annual premium of $330. If the company spends $20 per year to service such a policy, the probability of total loss for such a home in a given year is .002, and you assume that either total loss or no loss will occur, what is the company's expected annual gain (or profit) on each such policy?

Profits from a College Foundation Raffle *A college foundation raises funds by selling raffle tickets for a new car worth $36,000.*

13. If 600 tickets are sold for $120 each, determine
   (a) the expected *net* winnings of a person buying one of the tickets,
   (b) the total profit for the foundation, assuming they had to purchase the car,
   (c) the total profit for the foundation, assuming the car was donated.

14. For the raffle described in Exercise 13, if 720 tickets are sold for $120 each, determine
   (a) the expected *net* winnings of a person buying one of the tickets,
   (b) the total profit for the foundation, assuming they had to purchase the car,
   (c) the total profit for the foundation, assuming the car was donated.

Winnings and Profits of a Raffle *Five thousand raffle tickets are sold. One first prize of $1000, two second prizes of $500 each, and five third prizes of $100 each are to be awarded, with all winners selected randomly.*

15. If you purchased one ticket, what are your expected gross winnings?

16. If you purchased two tickets, what are your expected gross winnings?

17. If the tickets were sold for $1 each, how much profit goes to the raffle sponsor?

18. ***Expected Sales at a Theater Snack Bar*** A children's theater found in a random survey that 65 customers bought one snack bar item, 40 bought two items, 26 bought three items, 14 bought four items, and 18 avoided the snack bar altogether. Use this information to find the expected number of snack bar items per customer. (Round your answer to the nearest tenth.)

19. ***Expected Number of Children to Attend an Amusement Park*** An amusement park, considering adding some new attractions, conducted a study over several typical days and found that, of 10,000 families entering the park, 1020 brought just one child (defined as younger than age twelve), 3370 brought two children, 3510 brought three children, 1340 brought four children, 510 brought five children, 80 brought six children, and 170 brought no children at all. Find the expected number of children per family attending this park. (Round your answer to the nearest tenth.)

20. *Expected Sums of Randomly Selected Numbers* Five cards are numbered 1 through 5. Two of these cards are chosen randomly (without replacement), and the numbers on them are added. Find the expected value of this sum.

21. *Prospects for Electronics Jobs in a City* In a certain California city, projections for the next year are that there is a 20% chance that electronics jobs will increase by 1200, a 50% chance that they will increase by 500, and a 30% chance that they will decrease by 800. What is the expected change in the number of electronics jobs in that city in the next year?

22. *Expected Winnings in Keno* In one version of the game *keno*, the house has a pot containing 80 balls, numbered 1 through 80. A player buys a ticket for $1 and marks one number on it (from 1 to 80). The house then selects 20 of the 80 numbers at random. If the number selected by the player is among the 20 selected by the management, the player is paid $3.20. Find the expected net winnings for this game.

23. Refer to Examples 6 and 7. Considering the three different approaches (expected values, optimist, and pessimist), which one seems most reasonable to you, and why?

Contractor Decisions Based on Expected Profits *Dawn Casselberry, a commercial building contractor, will commit her company to one of three projects depending on her analysis of potential profits or losses as shown here.*

Project *A*		Project *B*		Project *C*	
Profit or Loss *x*	**Probability** *P(x)*	**Profit or Loss** *x*	**Probability** *P(x)*	**Profit or Loss** *x*	**Probability** *P(x)*
$40,000	.10	$0	.20	$60,000	.65
180,000	.60	210,000	.35	340,000	.35
250,000	.30	290,000	.45		

Determine which project Dawn should choose according to each approach.

24. expected values   **25.** the optimist viewpoint   **26.** the pessimist viewpoint

Expected Winnings in a Game Show *A game show contestant is offered the option of receiving a computer system worth $2300, or accepting a chance to win either a luxury vacation worth $5000 or a boat worth $8000. If the second option is chosen the contestant's probabilities of winning the vacation or the boat are .20 and .15, respectively.*

27. If the contestant were to turn down the computer system and go for one of the other prizes, what would be the expected winnings?

28. Purely in terms of monetary value, what is the contestant's wiser choice?

Evaluating an Insurance Purchase *The promoter of an outdoor concert expects a gate profit of $100,000, unless it rains, which would reduce gate profit to $30,000. The probability of rain is .28. The promoter can purchase insurance coverage of $100,000 against rain losses for a premium of $25,000. Use this information for Exercises 29–32.*

29. Find the expected net profit when the insurance is purchased.

30. Find the expected net profit when the insurance is not purchased.

31. Based on expected values, which is the promoter's wiser choice?

32. If you were the promoter, would you base your decision on expected values? Explain your reasoning.

Expected Values in Business Accounts *The table below illustrates how a salesman for Levi Strauss & Co. rates his accounts by considering the existing volume of each account plus potential additional volume.* *

1	2	3	4	5	6	7
Account Number	Existing Volume	Potential Additional Volume	Probability of Getting Additional Volume	Expected Value of Additional Volume	Existing Volume plus Expected Value of Additional Volume	Classification
1	$15,000	$10,000	.25	$2500	$17,500	
2	40,000	0	—	—	40,000	
3	20,000	10,000	.20	2000		
4	50,000	10,000	.10	1000		
5	5000	50,000	.50			
6	0	100,000	.60			
7	30,000	20,000	.80			

Use the table to work Exercises 33–36.

33. Compute the missing expected values in column 5.

34. Compute the missing amounts in column 6.

35. In column 7, classify each account according to this scheme: Class A if the column 6 value is $55,000 or more; Class B if the column 6 value is at least $45,000 but less than $55,000; Class C if the column 6 value is less than $45,000.

36. Considering all seven of this salesman's accounts, compute the total additional volume he can "expect" to get.

37. *Expected Winnings in Keno* Recall that in the game keno of Exercise 22, the house randomly selects 20 numbers from the counting numbers 1–80. In the variation called 6-spot keno, the player pays 60¢ for his ticket and marks 6 numbers of his choice. If the 20 numbers selected by the house contain at least 3 of those chosen by the player, he gets a payoff according to this scheme.

3 of the player's numbers among the 20	$.35
4 of the player's numbers among the 20	2.00
5 of the player's numbers among the 20	60.00
6 of the player's numbers among the 20	1250.00

Find the player's expected net winnings in this game. [*Hint:* The four probabilities required here can be found using combinations (Section 1.3), the fundamental counting principle (Section 1.2), and the theoretical probability formula (Section 2.1).]

*This information was provided by James McDonald of Levi Strauss & Co., San Francisco.

EXTENSION
Estimating Probabilities by Simulation

		Second Parent	
		R	**r**
First Parent	**R**	RR	Rr
	r	rR	rr

An important area within probability theory is the process called **simulation.** It is possible to study a complicated, or unclear, phenomenon by *simulating,* or imitating, it with a simpler phenomenon involving the same basic probabilities.

For example, recall from Section 2.1 Mendel's discovery that when two Rr pea plants (red-flowered but carrying both red and white genes) are crossed, the offspring will have red flowers if an R gene is received from either parent, or from both. This is because red is dominant and white is recessive. Table 3, reproduced here in the margin, shows that three of the four equally likely possibilities result in red-flowered offspring.

Now suppose we want to know (or at least approximate) the probability that three offspring in a row will have red flowers. It is much easier (and quicker) to toss coins than to cross pea plants. And the equally likely outcomes, heads and tails, can be used to simulate the transfer of the equally likely genes, R and r. If we toss two coins, say a nickel and a penny, then we can interpret the results as follows.

hh $\Rightarrow$ RR $\Rightarrow$ red gene from first parent and red gene from second parent
$\Rightarrow$ red flowers

ht $\Rightarrow$ Rr $\Rightarrow$ red gene from first parent and white gene from second parent
$\Rightarrow$ red flowers

th $\Rightarrow$ rR $\Rightarrow$ white gene from first parent and red gene from second parent
$\Rightarrow$ red flowers

tt $\Rightarrow$ rr $\Rightarrow$ white gene from first parent and white gene from second parent
$\Rightarrow$ white flowers

Although nothing is certain for a few tosses, the law of large numbers indicates that larger and larger numbers of tosses should become better and better indicators of general trends in the genetic process.

Simulation methods, also called **"Monte Carlo" methods,** have been successfully used in many areas of scientific study for nearly a century. Most practical applications require huge numbers of random digits, so computers are used to produce them. A computer, however, cannot toss coins. It must use an algorithmic process, programmed into the computer, which is called a **random number generator.** It is very difficult to avoid all nonrandom patterns in the results, so the digits produced are called "pseudorandom" numbers. They must pass a battery of tests of randomness before being "approved for use."

Computer scientists and physicists have been encountering unexpected difficulties with even the most sophisticated random number generators. In recent years, researchers have discovered that a random number generator can pass all the tests, and work just fine for some simulation applications, but then produce faulty answers when used with a different simulation. Therefore, random number generators apparently cannot be approved for all uses in advance, but must be carefully checked along with each new simulation application proposed.

▌ EXAMPLE 1 Simulating Genetic Processes

Toss two coins 50 times and use the results to approximate the probability that the crossing of Rr pea plants will produce three successive red-flowered offspring.

SOLUTION

We actually tossed two coins 50 times and got the following sequence.

th, hh, th, tt, th, hh, ht, th, ht, th, hh, hh,

tt, th, hh, ht, ht, ht, ht, th, hh, hh, hh, tt,

ht, tt, hh, ht, ht, hh, tt, tt, tt, th, tt, tt, hh,

ht, ht, ht, hh, tt, th, hh, tt, hh, ht, tt, tt, tt

By the color interpretation described above, this gives the following sequence of flower colors in the offspring.

Only "both tails"
gives white.

→

red–red–red–white–red–red–red–red–red–red–red–red–
white–red–red–red–red–red–red–red–red–red–white–
red–white–red–red–red–red–white–white–white–red–white–white–red–
red–red–red–red–white–red–red–white–red–red–white–white–white

We now have an experimental list of 48 sets of three successive plants, the 1st, 2nd, and 3rd entries, then the 2nd, 3rd, and 4th entries, and so on. Do you see why there are 48 in all?

Now we just count up the number of these sets of three that are "red-red-red." Since there are 20 of those, our empirical probability of three successive red offspring, obtained through simulation, is $\frac{20}{48} = \frac{5}{12}$, or about .417. By applying the multiplication rule of probability (with all outcomes independent of one another), we find that the theoretical value is $(\frac{3}{4})^3 = \frac{27}{64}$, or about .422, so our approximation obtained by simulation is very close. ■

Pilots, astronauts, race car drivers, and others often receive a portion of their training in **simulators.** Some of these devices, which may be viewed as very technical, high-cost versions of video games, mimic, or imitate conditions to be encountered later in the "real world." A simulator session allows estimation of the likelihood, or probability, of different responses that the learner would display under actual conditions. Repeated sessions help the learner to develop more successful responses before actual equipment and lives are put at risk.

In human births boys and girls are (essentially) equally likely. Therefore, an individual birth can be simulated by tossing a fair coin, letting a head correspond to a girl and a tail to a boy.

EXAMPLE 2 Simulating Births with Coin Tossing

A sequence of 40 actual coin tosses produced the results below.

bbggb, gbbbg, gbgbb, bggbg, bbbbg, gbbgg, gbbgg, bgbbg

(For every head we have written g, for girl; for every tail, b, for boy.) Refer to this sequence to answer the following questions.

(a) How many pairs of two successive births are represented by the above sequence?

(b) How many of those pairs consist of both boys?

(c) Find the empirical probability, based on this simulation, that two successive births both will be boys. Give your answer to three decimal places.

SOLUTION

(a) Beginning with the 1st–2nd pair and ending with the 39th–40th pair, there are 39 pairs.

(b) Observing the sequence of boys and girls, we count 11 pairs of two consecutive boys.

(c) Utilizing parts (a) and (b), we have $\frac{11}{39} \approx .282$. ■

FIGURE 12

Another way to simulate births is to generate a random sequence of digits, perhaps interpreting even digits as girls and odd digits as boys. The digits might be generated by spinning the spinner in Figure 12. It turns out that many kinds of phenomena can be simulated using random digits, so we can save lots of effort by using the spinner to obtain a table of random digits, like in Table 20 on the next page, and then use that table to carry out any simulation experiment that is needed. Notice that the 250 random digits in Table 20 have been grouped conveniently so that we can easily follow down a column or across a row.

TABLE 20	
→ 51592	73219 ←
77876	55707 ←
36500	48007
40571	65191 ←
04822	06772
→ 53033	94928
92080	15709 ←
01587	39922
36006	96365
63698	14655
→ 17297	65587
22841	76905
→ 91979	12369
96480	54219
74949	89329
76896	90060
47588	06975
45521	05050
02472	69774
55184	78351 ←
40177	11464
84861	84086
86937	51497 ←
20931	12307
22454	68009

EXAMPLE 3 Simulating Births with Random Numbers

A couple plans to have five children. Use random number simulation to estimate the probability they will have more than three boys.

SOLUTION

Let each sequence of five digits, as they appear in Table 20, represent a family with five children, and (arbitrarily) associate odd digits with boys, even digits with girls. (Recall that 0 is even.) Verify that, of the fifty families simulated, only the ten marked with arrows have more than 3 boys (4 boys or 5 boys). Therefore, the estimated (empirical) probability is

$$P(\text{more than 3 boys}) = \frac{10}{50} = .20.$$

The theoretical value for the probability estimated in Example 3, above, would be the same as that obtained in Example 3 of Section 2.4. It was .1875. So our estimate above was fairly close. In light of the law of large numbers, a larger sampling of random digits (more than 50 simulated families) would most likely yield a closer approximation. Extensive tables of random digits are available in statistical research publications. Computers can also be programmed to generate sequences of "pseudo-random" digits, which serve the same purposes. In most simulation experiments, much larger samples than we are using here are necessary to obtain reliable results.

EXAMPLE 4 Simulating Card Drawing with Random Numbers

Use random number simulation to estimate the probability that two cards drawn from a standard deck with replacement will both be of the same suit.

SOLUTION

Use this correspondence: 0 and 1 mean clubs, 2 and 3 mean diamonds, 4 and 5 mean hearts, 6 and 7 mean spades, 8 and 9 are disregarded. Now read down the columns of Table 20. Suppose we (arbitrarily) use the first digit of each five-digit group. The first time from top to bottom gives the sequence

$$5\text{–}7\text{–}3\text{–}4\text{–}0\text{–}5\text{–}0\text{–}3\text{–}6\text{–}1\text{–}2\text{–}7\text{–}7\text{–}4\text{–}4\text{–}0\text{–}5\text{–}4\text{–}2\text{–}2.$$

First digits of the left groups

(Five 8s and 9s were omitted.) Starting again at the top, we obtain

$$7\text{–}5\text{–}4\text{–}6\text{–}0\text{–}1\text{–}3\text{–}1\text{–}6\text{–}7\text{–}1\text{–}5\text{–}0\text{–}0\text{–}6\text{–}7\text{–}1\text{–}5\text{–}1\text{–}6.$$

First digits of the right groups

(Again, there happened to be five 8s and 9s.) This 40-digit sequence of digits yields the sequence of suits shown next.

5 gives hearts, 7 gives spades, 3 gives diamonds, and so on.

hearts–spades–diamonds–hearts–clubs–hearts–clubs–diamonds–spades–
clubs–diamonds–spades–spades–hearts–hearts–clubs–hearts–hearts–
diamonds–diamonds–spades–hearts–hearts–spades–clubs–clubs–
diamonds–clubs–spades–spades–clubs–hearts–clubs–clubs–spades–
spades–clubs–hearts–clubs–spades

Verify that, of the 39 successive pairs of suits (hearts–spades, spades–diamonds, diamonds–hearts, etc.), 9 of them are pairs of the same suit. This makes the estimated probability $\frac{9}{39} \approx .23$. (For comparison, the theoretical value is .25.)

EXTENSION EXERCISES

1. *Simulating Pea Plant Reproduction with Coin Tossing* Explain why, in Example 1, fifty tosses of the coins produced only 48 sets of three successive offspring.

2. *Simulating Pea Plant Reproduction with Coin Tossing* Use the sequence of flower colors of Example 1 to approximate the probability that *four* successive offspring all will have red flowers.

3. *Comparing the Likelihoods of Girl and Boy Births* Should the probability of two successive girl births be any different from that of two successive boy births?

4. *Finding Empirical Probability* Simulate 40 births by tossing coins yourself, and obtain an empirical probability for two successive girls.

5. *Simulating Boy and Girl Children with Random Numbers* Use Table 20 to simulate fifty families with three children. Let 0–4 correspond to boys and 5–9 to girls, and use the middle three digits of the left hand groupings (159, 787, 650, and so on). Estimate the probability of exactly two boys in a family of three children. Compare the estimation with the theoretical probability, which is $\frac{3}{8} = .375$. ·

Simulating One-and-One Foul Shooting with Random Numbers Exercises 71–73 of Section 2.3 involved one-and-one foul shooting in basketball. Susan, who had a 70% foul-shooting record, had probabilities of scoring 0, 1, or 2 points of .30, .21, and .49, respectively.

  Use Table 20 (with digits 0–6 representing hit and 7–9 representing miss) to simulate 50 one-and-one shooting opportunities for Susan. Begin at the top of the first column (5, 7, 3, etc., to the bottom), then move to the second column (1, 7, 6, etc.), going until 50 one-and-one opportunities are obtained. (Some "opportunities" involve one shot while others involve two shots.) Keep a tally of the numbers of times 0, 1, and 2 points are scored.

Number of Points	Tally
0	
1	
2	

From the tally, find the empirical probability that, on a given opportunity, Susan will score as follows. (Round to two decimal places.)

6. no points

7. 1 point

8. 2 points

Determining the Path of a Random Walk Using a Die and a Coin Exercises 47–54 of Section 2.4 illustrated a simple version of the idea of a "random walk." Atomic particles released in nuclear fission also move in a random fashion. During World War II, John von Neumann and Stanislaw Ulam used simulation with random numbers to study particle motion in nuclear reactions. Von Neumann coined the name "Monte Carlo" for the methods used, and since then the terms "Monte Carlo methods" and "simulation methods" have often been used with very little distinction.

  The figure suggests a model for random motion in two dimensions. Assume that a particle moves in a series of 1-unit "jumps," each one in a random direction, any one of 12 equally likely possibilities. One way to choose directions is to roll a fair die and toss a fair coin. The die determines one of the directions 1–6, coupled with heads on the coin. Tails on the coin reverses the direction of the die, so that the die coupled with tails gives directions 7–12. Thus 3h (meaning 3 with the die and heads with the coin) gives direction 3; 3t gives direction 9 (opposite to 3); and so on.

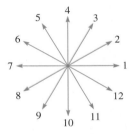

9. Simulate the motion described above with 10 rolls of a die (and tosses of a coin). Draw the 10-jump path you get. Make your drawing accurate enough so you can estimate (by measuring) how far from its starting point the particle ends up.

10. Repeat the experiment of Exercise 9 four more times. Measure distance from start to finish for each of the 5 "random trips." Add these 5 distances and divide the sum by 5, to arrive at an "expected net distance" for such a trip.

For Exercises 11 and 12, consider another two-dimensional random walk governed by the following conditions.

1. *Start out from a given street corner, and travel one block north. At each intersection:*

2. *Turn left with probability $\frac{1}{6}$.*

3. *Go straight with probability* $\frac{2}{6}(=\frac{1}{3})$.

4. *Turn right with probability* $\frac{3}{6}(=\frac{1}{2})$.

(Never turn around.)

11. *A Random Walk Using a Fair Die* Explain how a fair die could be used to simulate this random walk.

12. *A Random Walk Using a Random Number Table* Use Table 20 to simulate this random walk. For every 1 encountered in the table, turn left and proceed for another block. For every 2 or 3, go straight and proceed for another block. For every 4, 5, or 6, turn right and proceed for another block. Disregard all other digits, that is, 0s, 7s, 8s, and 9s. (Do you see how this scheme satisfies the probabilities given before Exercise 11?) This time begin at the upper right corner of the table, running down the column 9, 7, 7, and so on, to the bottom. Then start at the top of the next column to the left, 1, 0, 0, and so on, to the bottom. When these two columns of digits are used up, stop the "walk." Describe, in terms of distance and direction, where you have ended up relative to your starting point.

COLLABORATIVE INVESTIGATION

Finding Empirical Values of π

The information in this investigation was obtained from Burton's History of Mathematics: An Introduction, Third Edition, by David M. Burton, published by Wm. C. Brown, 1995, page 440.

The following problem was posed by Georges Louis Leclerc, Comte de Buffon (1707–1788) in his *Histoire Naturelle* in 1777. A large plane area is ruled with equidistant parallel lines, the distance between two consecutive lines of the series being a. A thin needle of length $\ell < a$ is tossed randomly onto the plane. What is the probability that the needle will intersect one of these lines?

The answer to this problem is found using integral calculus, and the probability p is shown to be $p = \frac{2\ell}{\pi a}$. Solving for π gives us the formula

$$\pi = \frac{2\ell}{pa}, \qquad (1)$$

which can be used to approximate the value of π experimentally. This was first observed by Pierre Simon de Laplace, and such an experiment was carried out by Johann Wolf, a professor of astronomy at Bern, in about 1850. In this investigation, we will perform a similar experiment.

See www.angelfire.com/wa/hurben/buff.html for a dynamic illustration of this Buffon Needle Problem.

Topics for Discussion

Divide the class into groups of 3 or 4 students each. Each group will need the following materials.

1. a sheet of paper with a series of parallel lines evenly spaced across it

2. a thin needle, or needlelike object, with a length less than the distance between adjacent parallel lines on the paper

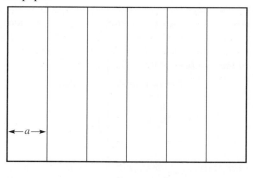

Each group should carry out these steps:

1. Measure and record the distance between lines (*a*) and the length of the needle (*ℓ*), using the same units for both.

2. Assign one member to drop the needle onto the paper, another to determine whether the needle "hits" a line or not, and another to keep a tally of hits and misses.

3. Discuss ways to minimize bias so that the position and orientation of the dropped needle will be as random as possible.

4. Drop the needle 100 times, and record the number of hits.

5. Calculate the probability $p = $ (number of hits)/100. Is this probability value theoretical or empirical?

6. Enter the calculated value of p and the measured values of a and $ℓ$ into formula (1) to obtain a value of π. Round this value to four decimal places.

Now come back together as a class and record the various values obtained for π. Discuss the following questions.

1. The correct value of π, to four decimal places, is 3.1416. Which value of π, reported by the various groups, is most accurate? How far off is it?

2. Was it necessary to drop the needle 100 times, or could more or fewer tosses have been used?

3. Wolf tossed his needle 5000 times and it hit a line 2532 times, leading to an experimental value of π equal to 3.1596. How far off was Wolf's value?

4. How could the experiment be modified to produce "better" values for π?

5. Why could different groups use different $ℓ$ to a ratios and still all obtain legitimate approximations for π?

CHAPTER 2 TEST

1. Explain the difference between *empirical* and *theoretical* probabilities.

2. State the *law of large numbers,* and use coin tossing to illustrate it.

Drawing Cards *A single card is chosen at random from a standard 52-card deck. Find the odds against its being each of the following.*

3. a heart   4. a red queen

5. a king or a black face card

Genetics of Cystic Fibrosis *The chart represents genetic transmission of cystic fibrosis. C denotes a normal gene while c denotes a cystic fibrosis gene. (Normal is dominant.) Both parents in this case are Cc, which means that they inherited one of each gene, and are therefore carriers but do not have the disease.*

		Second Parent	
		C	c
First Parent	C		Cc
	c		

6. Complete the chart, showing all four equally likely gene combinations.

7. Find the probability that a child of these parents will also be a carrier without the disease.

8. What are the odds that a child of these parents actually will have cystic fibrosis?

Days Off for Pizza Parlor Workers *The manager of a pizza parlor (which operates seven days a week) allows each of three employees to select one day off next week. Assuming the selection is done randomly and independently, find the probability of each event.*

9. All three select different days.

10. All three select the same day, given that all three select a day beginning with the same letter.

11. Exactly two of them select the same day.

Building Numbers from Sets of Digits *Two numbers are randomly selected without replacement from the set* {1, 2, 3, 4, 5}. *Find the probability of each event.*

12. Both numbers are even.

13. Both numbers are prime.

14. The sum of the two numbers is odd.

15. The product of the two numbers is odd.

Selecting Committees *A three-member committee is selected randomly from a group consisting of three men and two women.*

16. Let x denote the number of men on the committee, and complete the probability distribution table.

x	$P(x)$
0	0
1	
2	
3	

17. Find the probability that the committee members are not all men.

18. Find the expected number of men on the committee.

Rolling Dice *A pair of dice are rolled. Find the following.*

19. the probability of "doubles" (the same number on both dice)

20. the odds in favor of a sum greater than 2

21. the odds against a sum of "7 or 11"

22. the probability of a sum that is even and less than 5

Making Par in Golf *Greg Brueck has a .78 chance of making par on each hole of golf that he plays. Today he plans to play just three holes. Find the probability of each event. Round answers to three decimal places.*

23. He makes par on all three holes.

24. He makes par on exactly two of the three holes.

25. He makes par on at least one of the three holes.

26. He makes par on the first and third holes but not on the second.

Drawing Cards *Two cards are drawn, without replacement, from a standard 52-card deck. Find the probability of each event.*

27. Both cards are red.

28. Both cards are the same color.

29. The second card is a queen, given that the first card is an ace.

30. The first card is a face card and the second is black.

ANSWERS TO SELECTED EXERCISES

CHAPTER 1 Counting Methods

1.1 Exercises (Pages 8–11)

1. *AB, AC, AD, AE, BA, BC, BD, BE, CA, CB, CD, CE, DA, DB, DC, DE, EA, EB, EC, ED*;
20 ways **3.** *AC, AE, BC, BE, CA, CB, CD, DC, DE, EA, EB, ED*; 12 ways **5.** *ACE, AEC, BCE, BEC, DCE, DEC*; 6 ways
7. *ABC, ABD, ABE, ACD, ACE, ADE, BCD, BCE, BDE, CDE*; 10 ways **9.** 1 **11.** 3
13. 5 **15.** 5 **17.** 3 **19.** 1
21. 18 **23.** 15

25.

	1	2	3	4	5	6
1	11	12	13	14	15	16
2	21	22	23	24	25	26
3	31	32	33	34	35	36
4	41	42	43	44	45	46
5	51	52	53	54	55	56
6	61	62	63	64	65	66

27. 11, 22, 33, 44, 55, 66 **29.** 11, 13, 23, 31, 41, 43, 53, 61 **31.** 16, 25, 36, 64
33. 16, 32, 64

35. **(a)** tttt **(b)** hhhh, hhht, hhth, hhtt, hthh, htht, htth, thhh, thht, thth, tthh **(c)** httt, thtt, ttht, ttth, tttt **(d)** hhhh, hhht, hhth, hhtt, hthh, htht, htth, httt, thhh, thht, thth, thtt, tthh, ttht, ttth

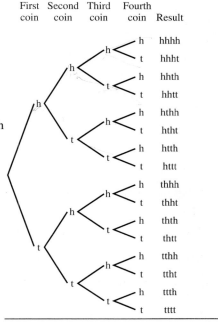

37. 16 **39.** 36 **41.** 17 **43.** 72 **45.** 12 **47.** 10 **49.** 6 **51.** 3 **53.** 54 **55.** 18
57. 138 **59.** 16 **61.** 13 **63.** 4 **65.** 883 **67.** 3 **69. (a)** Determine the number of ordered pairs of digits that can be selected from the set $\{1, 2, 3, 4, 5, 6\}$ if repetition of digits is allowed. **(b)** Determine the number of ordered pairs of digits that can be selected from the set $\{1, 2, 3, 4, 5, 6\}$ if the selection is done with replacement.
71. (a) Find the number of ways to select three letters from the set $\{A, B, C, D, E\}$ if repetition of letters is not allowed. **(b)** Find the number of ways to select three letters from the set $\{A, B, C, D, E\}$ if the selection is done without replacement.

1.2 Exercises (Pages 19–22)

1. Answers will vary. **3. (a)** no **(b)** Answers will vary. **5. (a)** no **(b)** Answers will vary. **7.** 24
9. 336 **11.** 20 **13.** 84 **15.** 840 **17.** 39,916,800 **19.** 95,040 **21.** 1716 **23.** 184,756
25. $4.151586701 \times 10^{12}$ **27.** 362,880 **29.** 1680 **31.** $2^3 = 8$ **33.** Answers will vary.
35. $6^3 = 216$ **37.** $5! = 120$ **39.** $3 \cdot 2 = 6$ **41.** $3 \cdot 3 = 9$ **43.** $3 \cdot 2 \cdot 1 = 6$ **45.** $4 \cdot 2 \cdot 3 = 24$
47. $2^6 = 64$ **49.** $3 \cdot 3 \cdot 4 \cdot 5 = 180$ **51.** $3 \cdot 3 \cdot 4 \cdot 3 = 108$ **53.** $3 \cdot 3 \cdot 1 \cdot 3 = 27$
55. $2 \cdot 5 \cdot 6 = 60$ **57.** $5! = 120$ **59. (a)** 6 **(b)** 5 **(c)** 4 **(d)** 3 **(e)** 2 **(f)** 1; 720 **61. (a)** 3
(b) 3 **(c)** 2 **(d)** 2 **(e)** 1 **(f)** 1; 36 **63.** Answers will vary. **65.** 450; no

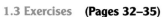

1.3 Exercises (Pages 32–35)

1. 840 **3.** 495 **5.** 1,028,160 **7.** 70 **9.** $1.805037696 \times 10^{11}$ **11.** Answers will vary.
13. Answers will vary. **15. (a)** permutation **(b)** permutation **(c)** combination **(d)** combination
(e) permutation **(f)** combination **(g)** permutation **17.** $_8P_5 = 6720$ **19.** $_{12}P_2 = 132$
21. $_{25}P_5 = 6,375,600$ **23. (a)** $_4P_4 = 24$ **(b)** $_4P_4 = 24$ **25.** $_{18}C_5 = 8568$ **27. (a)** $_{13}C_5 = 1287$

(b) $_{26}C_5 = 65,780$ **(c)** 0 (impossible) **29. (a)** $_6C_3 = 20$ **(b)** $_6C_2 = 15$ **31.** $_{10}C_3 = 120$ **33. (a)** 5
(b) 9 **35.** $_{26}P_3 \cdot {}_{10}P_3 \cdot {}_{26}P_3 = 175,219,200,000$ **37.** $2 \cdot {}_{25}P_3 = 27,600$ **39.** $7 \cdot {}_{12}P_8 = 139,708,800$
41. (a) $7^7 = 823,543$ **(b)** $7! = 5040$ **43.** $_{25}C_3 \cdot {}_{22}C_4 \cdot {}_{18}C_5 \cdot {}_{13}C_6 \approx 2.473653743 \times 10^{14}$
45. $_{20}C_3 = 1140$ **47. (a)** $_7P_2 = 42$ **(b)** $3 \cdot 6 = 18$ **(c)** $_7P_2 \cdot 5 = 210$ **49.** $_8P_3 = 336$
51. (a) $_6C_2 \cdot {}_6C_3 \cdot {}_6C_4 = 4500$ **(b)** $3! \cdot {}_6C_2 \cdot {}_6C_3 \cdot {}_6C_4 = 27,000$ **53. (a)** $8! = 40,320$ **(b)** $2 \cdot 6! = 1440$
(c) $6! = 720$ **55. (a)** $2 \cdot 4! = 48$ **(b)** $3 \cdot 4! = 72$ **57.** Each equals 220. **59. (a)** 1 **(b)** Answers
will vary.

1.4 Exercises (Pages 40–42)

1. 6 **3.** 20 **5.** 56 **7.** 36 **9.** $_7C_1 \cdot {}_3C_3 = 7$ **11.** $_7C_3 \cdot {}_3C_1 = 105$ **13.** $_8C_3 = 56$
15. $_8C_5 = 56$ **17.** $_9C_4 = 126$ **19.** $1 \cdot {}_8C_3 = 56$ **21.** 1 **23.** 10 **25.** 5 **27.** 32 **29. (a)** All
are multiples of the row number. **(b)** The same pattern holds. **(c)** The same pattern holds. **31.** $\ldots 8, 13, 21, 34, \ldots$;
A number in this sequence is the sum of the two preceding terms. This is the Fibonacci sequence. **33.** row 8
35. The sum of the squares of the entries across the top row equals the entry at the bottom vertex.
37. Answers will vary. **Wording may vary for Exercises 39 and 41.** **39.** sum $= N$; Any entry in the array equals
the sum of the two entries immediately above it and immediately to its left. **41.** sum $= N$; Any entry in the array
equals the sum of the row of entries from the cell immediately above it to the left boundary of the array.

1.5 Exercises (Pages 47–49)

1. $2^4 - 1 = 15$ **3.** $2^7 - 1 = 127$ **5.** 120 **7.** $36 - 6 = 30$ **9.** $6 + 6 - 1 = 11$ **11.** 51
13. $90 - 9 = 81$ **15. (a)** $_8C_3 = 56$ **(b)** $_7C_3 = 35$ **(c)** $56 - 35 = 21$ **17.** $_7C_3 - {}_5C_3 = 25$
19. $_8P_3 - {}_6P_3 = 216$ **21.** $_{10}P_3 - {}_7P_3 = 510$ **23.** $_{25}C_4 - {}_{23}C_4 = 3795$ **25.** $13 + 4 - 1 = 16$
27. $30 + 15 - 10 = 35$ **29.** $2,598,960 - {}_{13}C_5 = 2,597,673$ **31.** $2,598,960 - {}_{40}C_5 = 1,940,952$
33. $_{12}C_0 + {}_{12}C_1 + {}_{12}C_2 = 79$ **35.** $2^{12} - 79 = 4017$ **37.** $26^3 \cdot 10^3 - {}_{26}P_3 \cdot {}_{10}P_3 = 6,344,000$
39. Answers will vary. **41.** $_4C_3 + {}_3C_3 + {}_5C_3 = 15$ **43.** $_{12}C_3 - 4 \cdot 3 \cdot 5 = 160$ **45.** Answers will vary.
47. Answers will vary. **49.** Answers will vary.

Chapter 1 Test (Pages 50–51)

1. $6 \cdot 7 \cdot 7 = 294$ **2.** $6 \cdot 7 \cdot 4 = 168$ **3.** $6 \cdot 6 \cdot 5 = 180$ **4.** $6 \cdot 5 \cdot 1 = 30$ end in 0; $5 \cdot 5 \cdot 1 = 25$ end
in 5; $30 + 25 = 55$ **5.** 13

6.

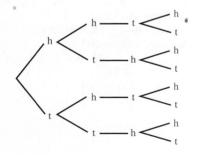

First Second Third Fourth
toss toss toss toss

7. $4! = 24$ **8.** 12 **9.** 120 **10.** 336 **11.** 11,880 **12.** 35 **13.** $_{26}P_5 = 7,893,600$
14. $32^5 = 33.554,432$ **15.** $_7P_4 = 840$ **16.** $3! = 6$ **17.** 120 **18.** 30,240 **19.** $_{12}C_4 = 495$
20. $_{12}C_2 \cdot {}_{10}C_2 = 2970$ **21.** $_{12}C_5 \cdot {}_7C_5 = 16,632$ **22.** $2^{12} - [{}_{12}C_0 + {}_{12}C_1 + {}_{12}C_2] = 4017$ **23.** $2^4 = 16$

24. $2^2 = 4$ **25.** $2 \cdot 2^2 = 8$ **26.** 8   **27.** 2   **28.** $16 - (1 + 4) = 11$ **29.** $_6C_3 = 20$
30. $_5C_2 = 10$ **31.** $2 \cdot {}_5C_3 = 20$ **32.** $_5C_2 = 10$ **33.** $_5C_4 + {}_2C_1 \cdot {}_5C_3 = 25$ **34.** Answers will vary.
35. $495 + 220 = 715$ **36.** the counting numbers   **37.** Answers will vary.

CHAPTER 2   Probability

2.1 Exercises   (Pages 61–65)

1. (a) $\dfrac{1}{3}$ (b) $\dfrac{1}{3}$ (c) $\dfrac{1}{3}$ **3.** (a) $\dfrac{1}{2}$ (b) $\dfrac{1}{3}$ (c) $\dfrac{1}{6}$ **5.** (a) $\{1, 2, 3\}$ (b) 2 (c) 1 (d) 3 (e) $\dfrac{2}{3}$ (f) 2 to 1

7. (a) $\{11, 12, 13, 21, 22, 23, 31, 32, 33\}$ (b) $\dfrac{2}{3}$ (c) $\dfrac{1}{3}$ (d) $\dfrac{1}{3}$ (e) $\dfrac{4}{9}$ **9.** (a) 4 to 7 (b) 5 to 6 (c) 2 to 9

11. (a) $\dfrac{1}{50}$ (b) $\dfrac{2}{50} = \dfrac{1}{25}$ (c) $\dfrac{3}{50}$ (d) $\dfrac{4}{50} = \dfrac{2}{25}$ (e) $\dfrac{5}{50} = \dfrac{1}{10}$ **13.** (a) $\dfrac{1}{36}$ (b) $\dfrac{2}{36} = \dfrac{1}{18}$ (c) $\dfrac{3}{36} = \dfrac{1}{12}$
(d) $\dfrac{4}{36} = \dfrac{1}{9}$ (e) $\dfrac{5}{36}$ (f) $\dfrac{6}{36} = \dfrac{1}{6}$ (g) $\dfrac{5}{36}$ (h) $\dfrac{4}{36} = \dfrac{1}{9}$ (i) $\dfrac{3}{36} = \dfrac{1}{12}$ (j) $\dfrac{2}{36} = \dfrac{1}{18}$ (k) $\dfrac{1}{36}$
15. (a) $\dfrac{34{,}244{,}000}{288{,}280{,}000} \approx .119$ (b) $\dfrac{288{,}280{,}000 - 34{,}244{,}000}{288{,}280{,}000} = \dfrac{254{,}036{,}000}{288{,}280{,}000} \approx .881$ **17.** Answers will vary.

19. $\dfrac{1}{4}$ **21.** $\dfrac{1}{4}$ **23.** (a) $\dfrac{3}{4}$ (b) $\dfrac{1}{4}$ **25.** $\dfrac{1}{250{,}000} = .000004$ **27.** $\dfrac{1}{4}$ **29.** $\dfrac{1}{4}$ **31.** $\dfrac{2}{4} = \dfrac{1}{2}$

33. $\dfrac{1}{500} = .002$ **35.** about 160   **37.** $\dfrac{2}{4} = \dfrac{1}{2}$ **39.** (a) 0 (b) no (c) yes   **41.** Answers will vary.

43. $\dfrac{12}{31}$ **45.** $\dfrac{36}{2{,}598{,}960} \approx .00001385$ **47.** $\dfrac{624}{2{,}598{,}960} \approx .00024010$ **49.** $\dfrac{1}{4} \cdot \dfrac{5108}{2{,}598{,}960} \approx .00049135$

51. (a) $\dfrac{5}{9}$ (b) $\dfrac{49}{144}$ (c) $\dfrac{5}{48}$ **53.** $3 \cdot 1 \cdot 2 \cdot 1 \cdot 1 \cdot 1 = 6; \dfrac{6}{720} = \dfrac{1}{120} \approx .0083$ **55.** $4 \cdot 3! \cdot 3! = 144;$

$\dfrac{144}{720} = \dfrac{1}{5} = .2$ **57.** $\dfrac{2}{{}_7C_2} = \dfrac{2}{21} \approx .095$ **59.** $\dfrac{{}_5C_3}{{}_{12}C_3} = \dfrac{1}{22} \approx .045$ **61.** $\dfrac{1}{{}_{36}P_3} \approx .000023$ **63.** $\dfrac{3}{28} \approx .107$

65. (a) $\dfrac{8}{9^2} = \dfrac{8}{81} \approx .099$ (b) $\dfrac{4}{{}_9C_2} = \dfrac{1}{9} \approx .111$ **67.** $\dfrac{9 \cdot 10}{9 \cdot 10^2} = \dfrac{1}{10}$

2.2 Exercises   (Pages 72–73)

1. yes   **3.** Answers will vary.   **5.** $\dfrac{1}{2}$ **7.** $\dfrac{5}{6}$ **9.** $\dfrac{2}{3}$ **11.** (a) $\dfrac{2}{13}$ (b) 2 to 11   **13.** (a) $\dfrac{11}{26}$ (b) 11 to 15

15. (a) $\dfrac{9}{13}$ (b) 9 to 4   **17.** $\dfrac{2}{3}$ **19.** $\dfrac{7}{36}$ **21.** $P(A) + P(B) + P(C) + P(D) = 1$ **23.** .005365

25. .971285   **27.** .76   **29.** .92   **31.** 6 to 19

33.

x	$P(x)$
3	.1
4	.1
5	.2
6	.2
7	.2
8	.1
9	.1

35. $n(A') = s - a$ **37.** $P(A) + P(A') = 1$ **39.** 180   **41.** $\dfrac{2}{3}$ **43.** 1

2.3 Exercises (Pages 82–85)

1. independent **3.** not independent **5.** independent **7.** $\dfrac{42}{100} = \dfrac{21}{50}$ **9.** $\dfrac{68}{100} = \dfrac{17}{25}$ **11.** $\dfrac{19}{34}$

13. $\dfrac{4}{7} \cdot \dfrac{4}{7} = \dfrac{16}{49}$ **15.** $\dfrac{2}{7} \cdot \dfrac{1}{7} = \dfrac{2}{49}$ **17.** $\dfrac{4}{7} \cdot \dfrac{3}{6} = \dfrac{2}{7}$ **19.** $\dfrac{1}{6}$ **21.** 0 **23.** $\dfrac{12}{51} = \dfrac{4}{17}$ **25.** $\dfrac{12}{52} \cdot \dfrac{11}{51} = \dfrac{11}{221}$

27. $\dfrac{4}{52} \cdot \dfrac{11}{51} = \dfrac{11}{663}$ **29.** $\dfrac{1}{3}$ **31.** 1 **33.** $\dfrac{3}{10}$ (the same) **35.** $\dfrac{1}{2} \cdot \dfrac{1}{2} \cdot \dfrac{1}{2} = \dfrac{1}{8}$ **37.** .640 **39.** .008

41. .95 **43.** .23 **45.** $\dfrac{1}{35}$ **47.** $\dfrac{3}{7}$ **49.** $\dfrac{3}{7}$ **51. (a)** $\dfrac{3}{4}$ **(b)** $\dfrac{1}{2}$ **(c)** $\dfrac{5}{16}$ **53.** .2704 **55.** .2496

57. Answers will vary. **59.** $\dfrac{1}{64} \approx .0156$ **61.** 10 **63.** .400 **65.** .080 **67.** $(.90)^4 = .6561$

69. $_4C_2 \cdot (.10) \cdot (.20) \cdot (.70)^2 = .0588$ **71.** .30 **73.** .49 **75.** Answers will vary.

2.4 Exercises (Pages 90–92)

1. $\dfrac{1}{8}$ **3.** $\dfrac{3}{8}$ **5.** $\dfrac{3}{4}$ **7.** $\dfrac{1}{2}$ **9.** $\dfrac{3}{8}$ **11.** $x; n; n$ **13.** $\dfrac{7}{128}$ **15.** $\dfrac{35}{128}$ **17.** $\dfrac{21}{128}$ **19.** $\dfrac{1}{128}$

21. $\dfrac{25}{72}$ **23.** $\dfrac{1}{216}$ **25.** .041 **27.** .268 **29.** Answers will vary. **31.** Answers will vary. **33.** .016

35. .020 **37.** .198 **39.** .448 **41.** .656 **43.** .002 **45.** .883 **47.** $\dfrac{1}{1024} \approx .001$ **49.** $\dfrac{45}{1024} \approx .044$

51. $\dfrac{210}{1024} \approx \dfrac{105}{512} \approx .205$ **53.** $\dfrac{772}{1024} \approx .754$

2.5 Exercises (Pages 100–103)

1. Answers will vary. **3.** $\dfrac{5}{2}$ **5.** \$1 **7.** 50¢ **9.** no (expected net winnings: $-\dfrac{3}{4}$¢) **11.** 1.72

13. (a) $-\$60$ **(b)** \$36,000 **(c)** \$72,000 **15.** 50¢ **17.** \$2500 **19.** 2.7 **21.** an increase of 250
23. Answers will vary. **25.** Project C **27.** \$2200 **29.** \$83,400 **31.** Purchase the insurance (because
$\$83,400 > \$80,400$). **33.** 25,000; 60,000; 16,000 **35.** C; C; C; B; C; A; B **37.** about -15¢

Extension Exercises (Pages 107–108)

1. Answers will vary. **3.** no **5.** $\dfrac{18}{50} = .36$ (This is quite close to .375, the theoretical value.) **7.** $\dfrac{11}{50} = .22$

9. Answers will vary. **11.** Answers will vary.

Chapter 2 Test (Pages 109–110)

1. Answers will vary. **2.** Answers will vary. **3.** 3 to 1 **4.** 25 to 1 **5.** 11 to 2 **6.** row 1: CC; row 2: cC, cc

7. $\dfrac{1}{2}$ **8.** 1 to 3 **9.** $\dfrac{7}{7} \cdot \dfrac{6}{7} \cdot \dfrac{5}{7} = \dfrac{30}{49}$ **10.** $\dfrac{7}{19}$ **11.** $1 - \left(\dfrac{30}{49} + \dfrac{1}{49}\right) = \dfrac{18}{49}$ **12.** $\dfrac{_2C_2}{_5C_2} = \dfrac{1}{10}$

13. $\dfrac{_3C_2}{_5C_2} = \dfrac{3}{10}$ **14.** $\dfrac{6}{10} = \dfrac{3}{5}$ **15.** $\dfrac{3}{10}$ **16.** $\dfrac{3}{10}; \dfrac{6}{10}; \dfrac{1}{10};$ **17.** $\dfrac{9}{10}$ **18.** $\dfrac{18}{10} = \dfrac{9}{5}$ **19.** $\dfrac{6}{36} = \dfrac{1}{6}$ **20.** 35 to 1

21. 7 to 2 **22.** $\dfrac{4}{36} = \dfrac{1}{9}$ **23.** $(.78)^3 \approx .475$ **24.** $_3C_2 (.78)^2(.22) \approx .402$ **25.** $1 - (.22)^3 \approx .989$

26. $(.78)(.22)(.78) \approx .134$ **27.** $\dfrac{25}{102}$ **28.** $\dfrac{25}{51}$ **29.** $\dfrac{4}{51}$ **30.** $\dfrac{3}{26}$